# RESIDENTIAL STEEL FRAMING
## CONSTRUCTION GUIDE

*Dedicated to:*
Troy, Travis, Trevor and Kassandra

**TECHNICAL PUBLICATIONS**
1442 E. Lincoln Ave., #319
Orange, CA 92665

(714) 632-7298 • FAX (714) 632-3096

Manufactured in the United States of America

# TABLE OF CONTENTS

(continued)

# FOREWORD

It is important for the user to understand that the details contained in this book are intended solely as a general guide with respect to residential steel framing. The details are not intended to be used as final approved engineering details. They should be reviewed and approved by licensed professional engineers and architects before actual implementation.

Details have been presented as generic and do not specifically refer to or recommend one manufacturer over another. One exception is the Gus Truss™, patented by Hemming Technologies.

The various details contained in this book represent standard framing techniques that have been developed and implemented over many years in the residential construction of custom homes, tract (production) homes and multi family units. The user should realize that other techniques are also used in the field of residential steel framing.

Steel framing provides an excellent alternative and opportunity to traditional wood framing and continues to gain momentum and popularity because of its many advantages. Steel framing is the wave of the future.

Finally, the author welcomes comments and suggestions from users as to how this book might be improved, and would appreciate notification of any inadvertent errors.

E.N. Lorre

# A. FLOOR SYSTEM

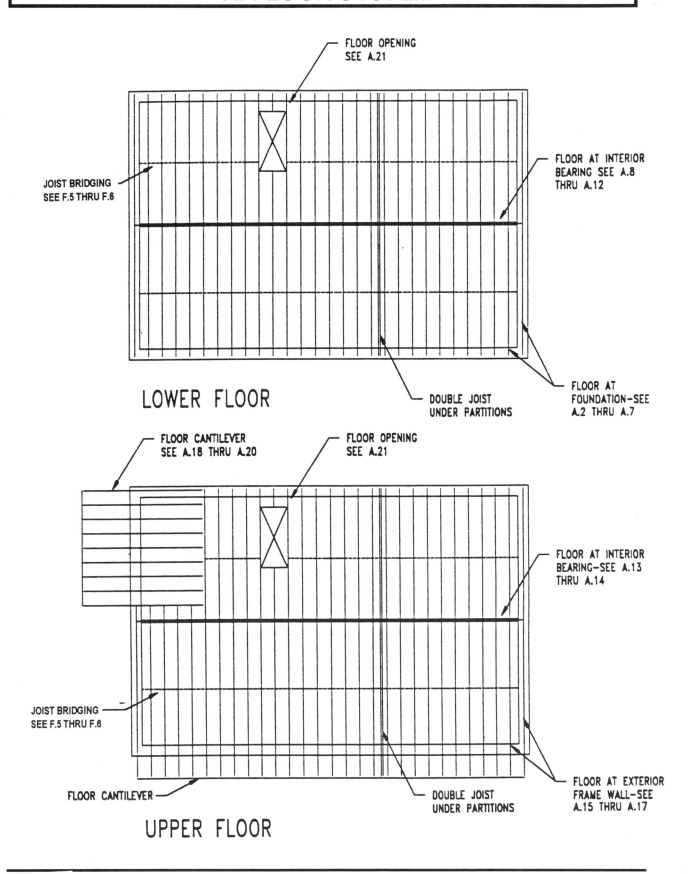

FLOOR OPENING
SEE A.21

JOIST BRIDGING
SEE F.5 THRU F.6

FLOOR AT INTERIOR
BEARING SEE A.8
THRU A.12

LOWER FLOOR

DOUBLE JOIST
UNDER PARTITIONS

FLOOR AT
FOUNDATION-SEE
A.2 THRU A.7

FLOOR CANTILEVER
SEE A.18 THRU A.20

FLOOR OPENING
SEE A.21

FLOOR AT INTERIOR
BEARING-SEE A.13
THRU A.14

JOIST BRIDGING
SEE F.5 THRU F.6

FLOOR CANTILEVER

DOUBLE JOIST
UNDER PARTITIONS

FLOOR AT EXTERIOR
FRAME WALL-SEE
A.15 THRU A.17

UPPER FLOOR

---

## TYPICAL FLOOR FRAMING SCHEMATICS        A.1

# A. FLOOR SYSTEM

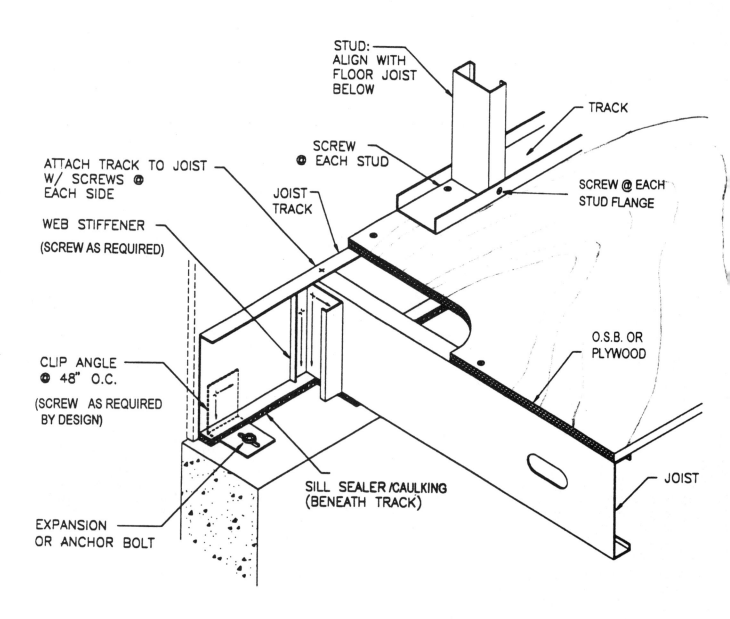

STUD:
ALIGN WITH
FLOOR JOIST
BELOW

TRACK

SCREW
@ EACH STUD

SCREW @ EACH
STUD FLANGE

ATTACH TRACK TO JOIST
W/ SCREWS @
EACH SIDE

JOIST
TRACK

WEB STIFFENER
(SCREW AS REQUIRED)

O.S.B. OR
PLYWOOD

CLIP ANGLE
@ 48" O.C.

(SCREW AS REQUIRED
BY DESIGN)

SILL SEALER /CAULKING
(BENEATH TRACK)

JOIST

EXPANSION
OR ANCHOR BOLT

**A.2**

## FLOOR JOIST TO TRACK
## BEARING ON FOUNDATION

# A. FLOOR SYSTEM

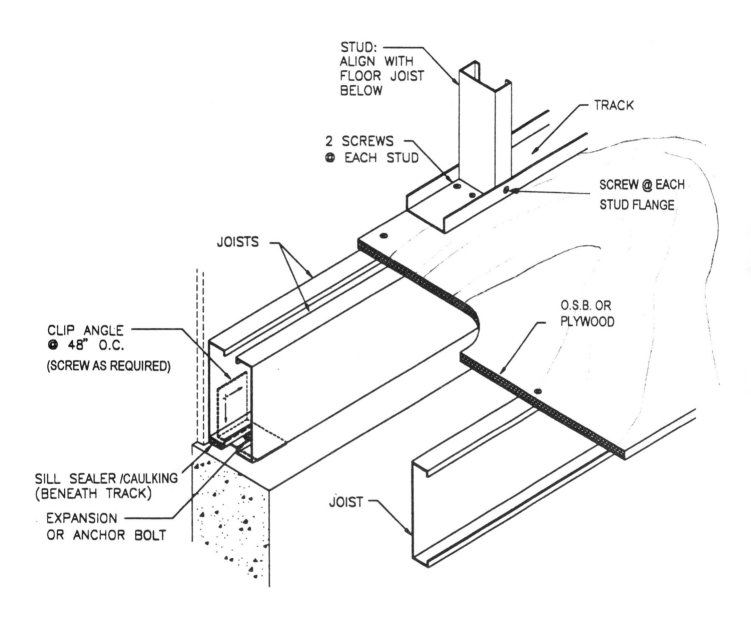

STUD:
ALIGN WITH
FLOOR JOIST
BELOW

TRACK

2 SCREWS
@ EACH STUD

SCREW @ EACH
STUD FLANGE

JOISTS

O.S.B. OR
PLYWOOD

CLIP ANGLE
@ 48" O.C.
(SCREW AS REQUIRED)

SILL SEALER /CAULKING
(BENEATH TRACK)

EXPANSION
OR ANCHOR BOLT

JOIST

---

## PARALLEL FLOOR JOISTS AT FOUNDATION

**A.3**

# A. FLOOR SYSTEM

CLIP ANGLE,
1/2" LESS THAN
JOIST DEPTH:
ATTACH TO CONCRETE
W/ EXPANSION OR
ANCHOR BOLTS.

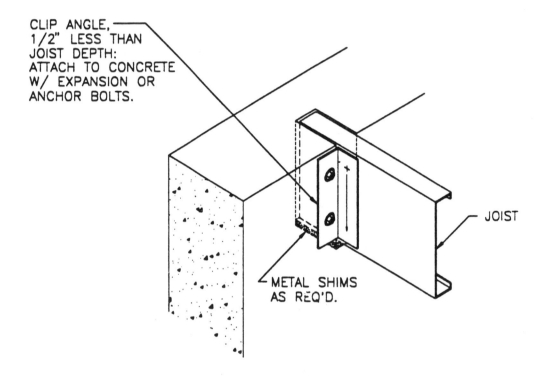

JOIST

METAL SHIMS
AS REQ'D.

# A. FLOOR SYSTEM

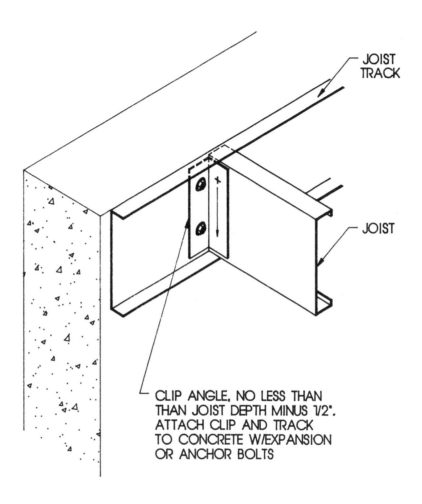

JOIST
TRACK

JOIST

CLIP ANGLE, NO LESS THAN
THAN JOIST DEPTH MINUS 1/2".
ATTACH CLIP AND TRACK
TO CONCRETE W/EXPANSION
OR ANCHOR BOLTS

## FLOOR JOIST FLUSH WITH
## TOP OF FOUNDATION

# A. FLOOR SYSTEM

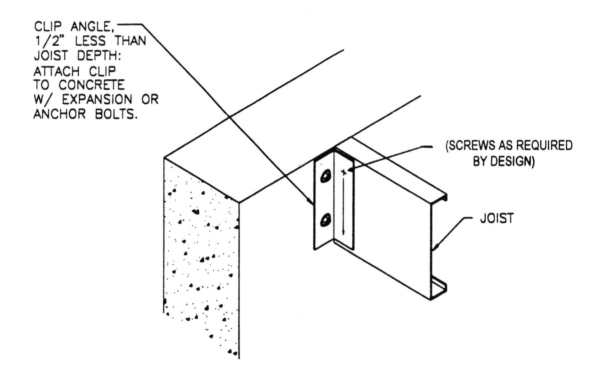

CLIP ANGLE,
1/2" LESS THAN
JOIST DEPTH:
ATTACH CLIP
TO CONCRETE
W/ EXPANSION OR
ANCHOR BOLTS.

(SCREWS AS REQUIRED
BY DESIGN)

JOIST

**FLOOR JOIST FLUSH WITH
TOP OF FOUNDATION**

# A. FLOOR SYSTEM

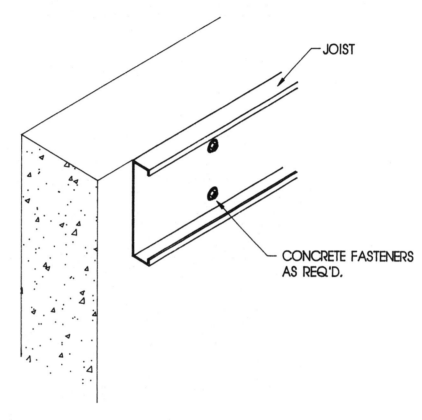

JOIST

CONCRETE FASTENERS
AS REQ'D.

NOTE:
PROVIDE SOLID BLOCKING
AND BRIDGING AS REQ'D.

**FLOOR JOIST FLUSH WITH
TOP OF FOUNDATION**

**A.7**

# A. FLOOR SYSTEM

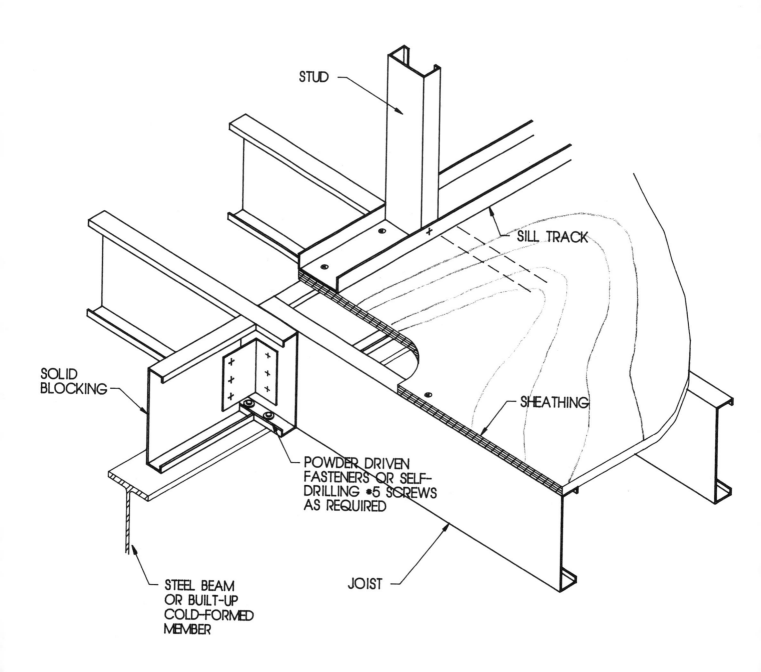

STUD

SILL TRACK

SOLID
BLOCKING

SHEATHING

POWDER DRIVEN
FASTENERS OR SELF-
DRILLING #5 SCREWS
AS REQUIRED

JOIST

STEEL BEAM
OR BUILT-UP
COLD-FORMED
MEMBER

**A.8**      FLOOR JOIST SPLICE OVER
STEEL OR BUILT-UP BEAM

# A. FLOOR SYSTEM

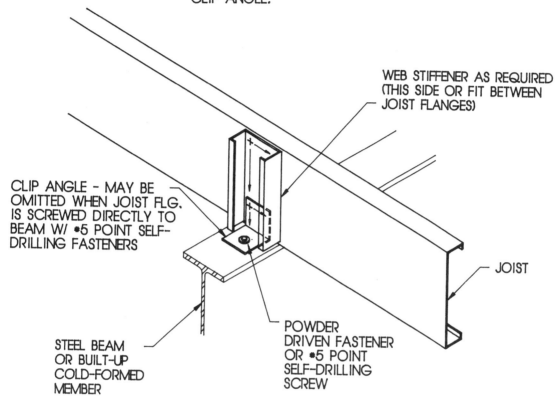

NOTE:
JOIST MAY BE SCREWED DIRECTLY TO BEAM USING MIN. 2-
#4 OR #5 POINT SELF DRILLING SCREWS IN LIEU OF A
CLIP ANGLE.

WEB STIFFENER AS REQUIRED
(THIS SIDE OR FIT BETWEEN
JOIST FLANGES)

CLIP ANGLE - MAY BE
OMITTED WHEN JOIST FLG.
IS SCREWED DIRECTLY TO
BEAM W/ #5 POINT SELF-
DRILLING FASTENERS

JOIST

STEEL BEAM
OR BUILT-UP
COLD-FORMED
MEMBER

POWDER
DRIVEN FASTENER
OR #5 POINT
SELF-DRILLING
SCREW

NOTES:
1. CONTINUOUS BRIDGING REQUIRED
   BETWEEN EACH JOIST ABOVE BEAM - SEE F.6.
   SOLID BLOCKING IN EVERY OTHER SPACE MAY
   BE USED IN LIEU OF BRIDGING.
2. WHEN WALL ABOVE, STUDS MUST ALIGN
   WITH JOISTS.
3. WEB STIFFENERS ARE NOT REQUIRED WHEN
   CONTINUOUS SOLID BLOCKING IS USED.

# A. FLOOR SYSTEM

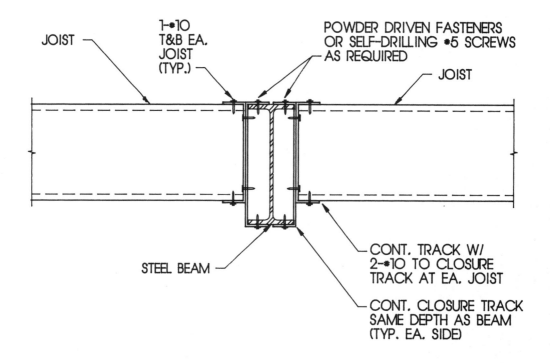

JOIST

1-#10 T&B EA. JOIST (TYP.)

POWDER DRIVEN FASTENERS OR SELF-DRILLING #5 SCREWS AS REQUIRED

JOIST

STEEL BEAM

CONT. TRACK W/ 2-#10 TO CLOSURE TRACK AT EA. JOIST

CONT. CLOSURE TRACK SAME DEPTH AS BEAM (TYP. EA. SIDE)

---

**A.10**     FLOOR JOIST FRAMED FLUSH
TO STEEL OR BUILT-UP BEAM

# A. FLOOR SYSTEM

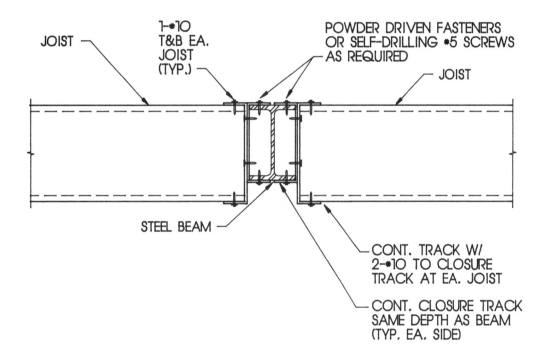

JOIST

1-#10
T&B EA.
JOIST
(TYP.)

POWDER DRIVEN FASTENERS
OR SELF-DRILLING #5 SCREWS
AS REQUIRED

JOIST

STEEL BEAM

CONT. TRACK W/
2-#10 TO CLOSURE
TRACK AT EA. JOIST

CONT. CLOSURE TRACK
SAME DEPTH AS BEAM
(TYP. EA. SIDE)

FLOOR JOIST FRAMED FLUSH
TO STEEL OR BUILT-UP BEAM

**A.11**

# A. FLOOR SYSTEM

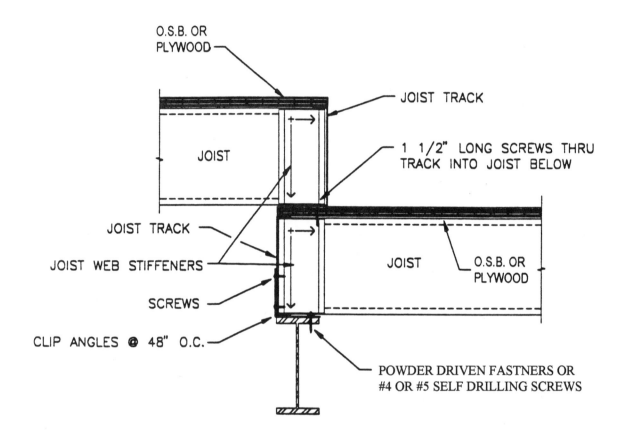

O.S.B. OR PLYWOOD

JOIST TRACK

JOIST

1 1/2" LONG SCREWS THRU TRACK INTO JOIST BELOW

JOIST TRACK

JOIST WEB STIFFENERS

JOIST

O.S.B. OR PLYWOOD

SCREWS

CLIP ANGLES @ 48" O.C.

POWDER DRIVEN FASTNERS OR #4 OR #5 SELF DRILLING SCREWS

---

**A.12**     FLOOR JOISTS AT SUNKEN FLOOR

# A. FLOOR SYSTEM

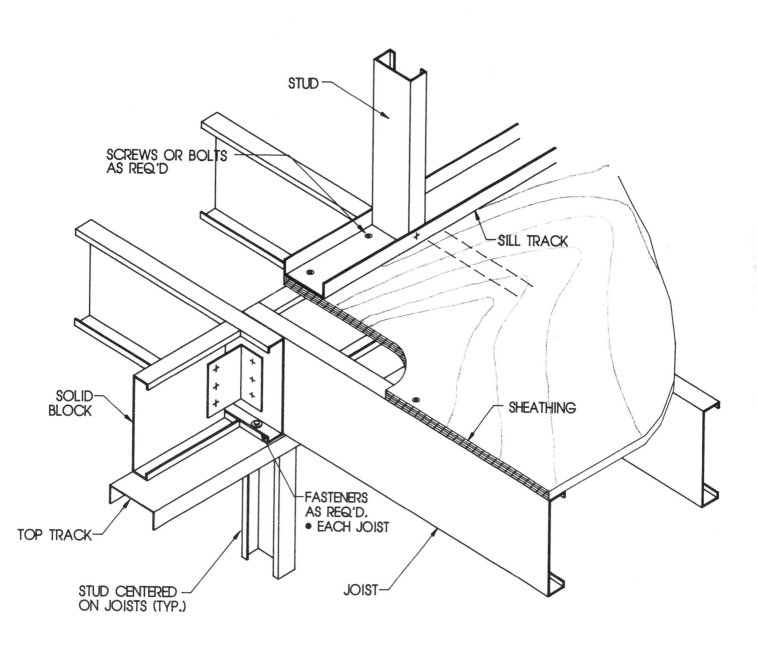

STUD

SCREWS OR BOLTS
AS REQ'D

SILL TRACK

SOLID
BLOCK

SHEATHING

TOP TRACK

FASTENERS
AS REQ'D.
● EACH JOIST

STUD CENTERED
ON JOISTS (TYP.)

JOIST

---

## FLOOR JOIST SPLICE OVER INTERIOR
## LOAD BEARING STUD WALL

**A.13**

# A. FLOOR SYSTEM

**NOTE:**
JOIST MAY BE SCREWED DIRECTLY TO TOP TRACK FROM
EITHER ABOVE OR BELOW THRU FLANGE WITH MIN. 2-#10
SCREWS.

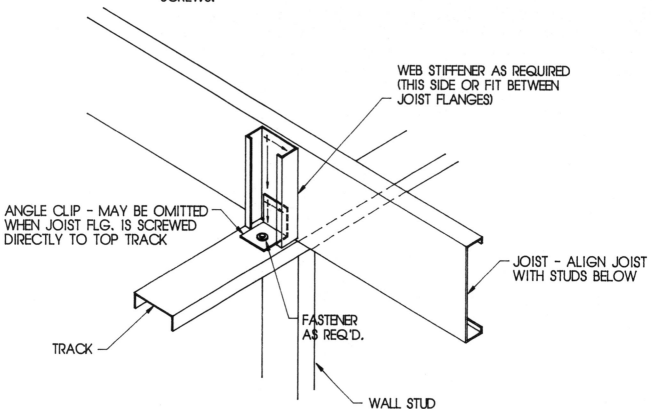

WEB STIFFENER AS REQUIRED
(THIS SIDE OR FIT BETWEEN
JOIST FLANGES)

ANGLE CLIP - MAY BE OMITTED
WHEN JOIST FLG. IS SCREWED
DIRECTLY TO TOP TRACK

JOIST - ALIGN JOIST
WITH STUDS BELOW

FASTENER
AS REQ'D.

TRACK

WALL STUD

NOTES:
1. SOLID BLOCKING MAY BE REQUIRED
   BETWEEN EACH JOIST

2. WEB STIFFENERS ARE NOT REQUIRED WHEN
   CONTINUOUS SOLID BLOCKING IS USED.

## CONTINUOUS FLOOR JOIST OVER
## LOAD BEARING STUD WALL

# A. FLOOR SYSTEM

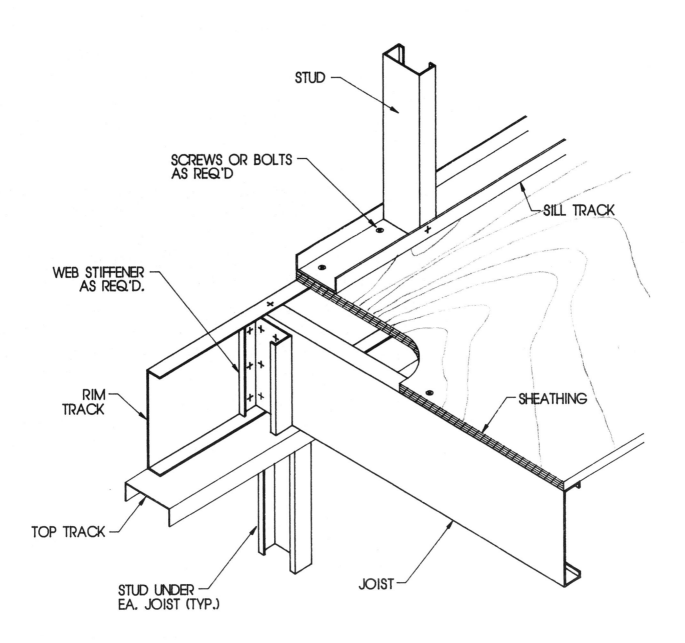

STUD

SCREWS OR BOLTS
AS REQ'D

SILL TRACK

WEB STIFFENER
AS REQ'D.

RIM
TRACK

SHEATHING

TOP TRACK

STUD UNDER
EA. JOIST (TYP.)

JOIST

# A. FLOOR SYSTEM

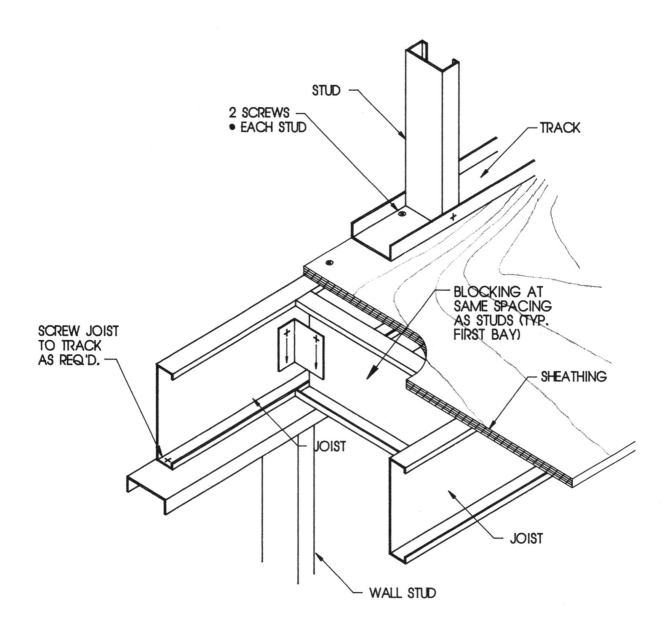

STUD

2 SCREWS • EACH STUD

TRACK

SCREW JOIST TO TRACK AS REQ'D.

BLOCKING AT SAME SPACING AS STUDS (TYP. FIRST BAY)

SHEATHING

JOIST

JOIST

WALL STUD

**A.16**     FLOOR JOIST PARALLEL TO EXTERIOR WALL
BEARING ON FOUNDATION

# A. FLOOR SYSTEM

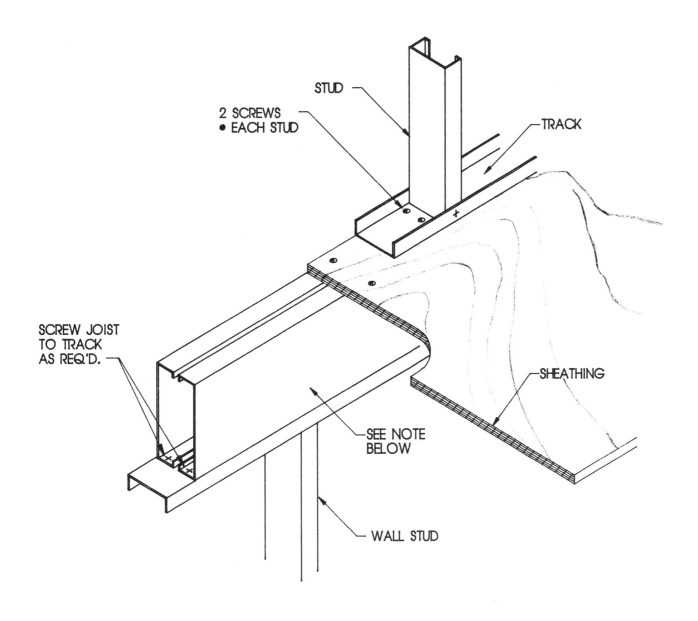

STUD

2 SCREWS
● EACH STUD

TRACK

SCREW JOIST
TO TRACK
AS REQ'D.

SHEATHING

SEE NOTE
BELOW

WALL STUD

NOTE:
RIM JOIST MAY BE DOUBLED AS SHOWN AND MAY BE UTILIZED TO ELIMINATE
THE NEED FOR ADDITIONAL DOOR OR WINDOW HEADERS. THIS DETAIL MAY ALSO
BE USED WHERE FIRE RATED WALL CONSTRUCTION IS REQUIRED.

---

## FLOOR JOIST PARALLEL TO EXTERIOR WALL BEARING ON FOUNDATION (ALTERNATE)

**A.16a**

# A. FLOOR SYSTEM

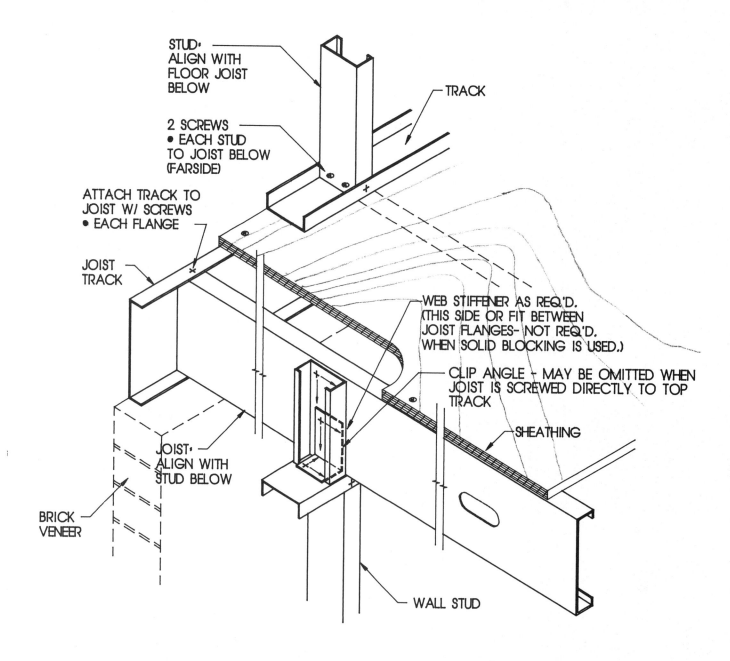

STUD·
ALIGN WITH
FLOOR JOIST
BELOW

TRACK

2 SCREWS
● EACH STUD
TO JOIST BELOW
(FARSIDE)

ATTACH TRACK TO
JOIST W/ SCREWS
● EACH FLANGE

JOIST
TRACK

WEB STIFFENER AS REQ'D.
(THIS SIDE OR FIT BETWEEN
JOIST FLANGES· NOT REQ'D.
WHEN SOLID BLOCKING IS USED.)

CLIP ANGLE - MAY BE OMITTED WHEN
JOIST IS SCREWED DIRECTLY TO TOP
TRACK

SHEATHING

JOIST·
ALIGN WITH
STUD BELOW

BRICK
VENEER

WALL STUD

NOTES·
1. PROVIDE CONT. BRIDGING
   BETWEEN EACH JOIST
   AT LOWER WALL - SEE F.6.
2. SOLID BLOCKING IN EVERY
   OTHER SPACE MAY BE USED
   IN LIEU OF BRIDGING - SEE F.4
3. WHERE AXIAL LOAD BEARING
   MEMBERS DO NOT ALIGN
   VERTICALLY PROVIDE DETAIL F.1

**A.17**  CANTILEVERED FLOOR JOIST AT BRICK VENEER

# A. FLOOR SYSTEM

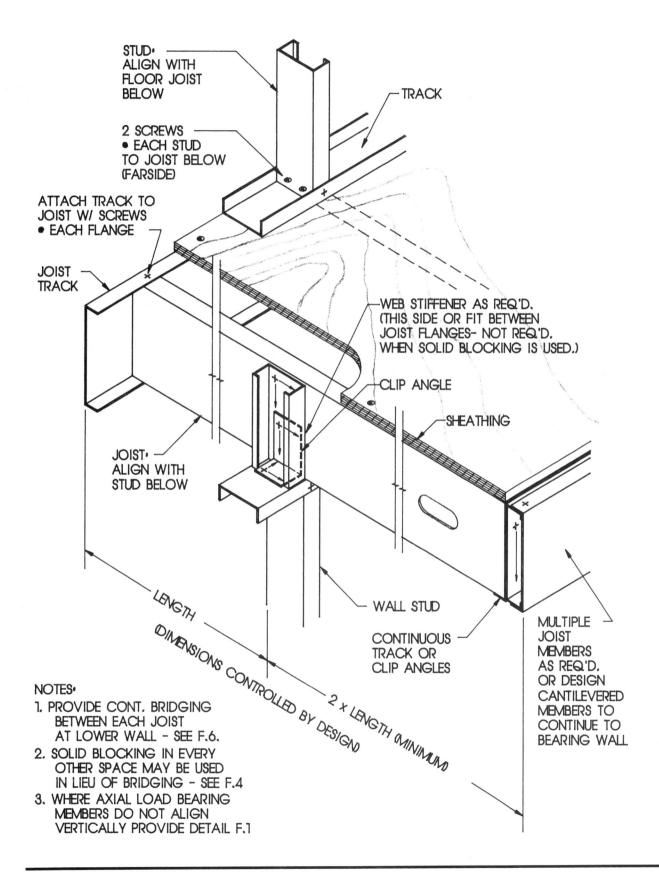

STUD:
ALIGN WITH
FLOOR JOIST
BELOW

2 SCREWS
● EACH STUD
TO JOIST BELOW
(FARSIDE)

ATTACH TRACK TO
JOIST W/ SCREWS
● EACH FLANGE

JOIST
TRACK

TRACK

WEB STIFFENER AS REQ'D.
(THIS SIDE OR FIT BETWEEN
JOIST FLANGES- NOT REQ'D.
WHEN SOLID BLOCKING IS USED.)

CLIP ANGLE

SHEATHING

JOIST:
ALIGN WITH
STUD BELOW

WALL STUD

CONTINUOUS
TRACK OR
CLIP ANGLES

MULTIPLE
JOIST
MEMBERS
AS REQ'D.
OR DESIGN
CANTILEVERED
MEMBERS TO
CONTINUE TO
BEARING WALL

LENGTH

(DIMENSIONS CONTROLLED BY DESIGN)

2 x LENGTH (MINIMUM)

NOTES:
1. PROVIDE CONT. BRIDGING
   BETWEEN EACH JOIST
   AT LOWER WALL - SEE F.6.
2. SOLID BLOCKING IN EVERY
   OTHER SPACE MAY BE USED
   IN LIEU OF BRIDGING - SEE F.4
3. WHERE AXIAL LOAD BEARING
   MEMBERS DO NOT ALIGN
   VERTICALLY PROVIDE DETAIL F.1

## CANTILEVERED FLOOR JOIST
## AT FLUSH BALCONY FLOOR

**A.18**

# A. FLOOR SYSTEM

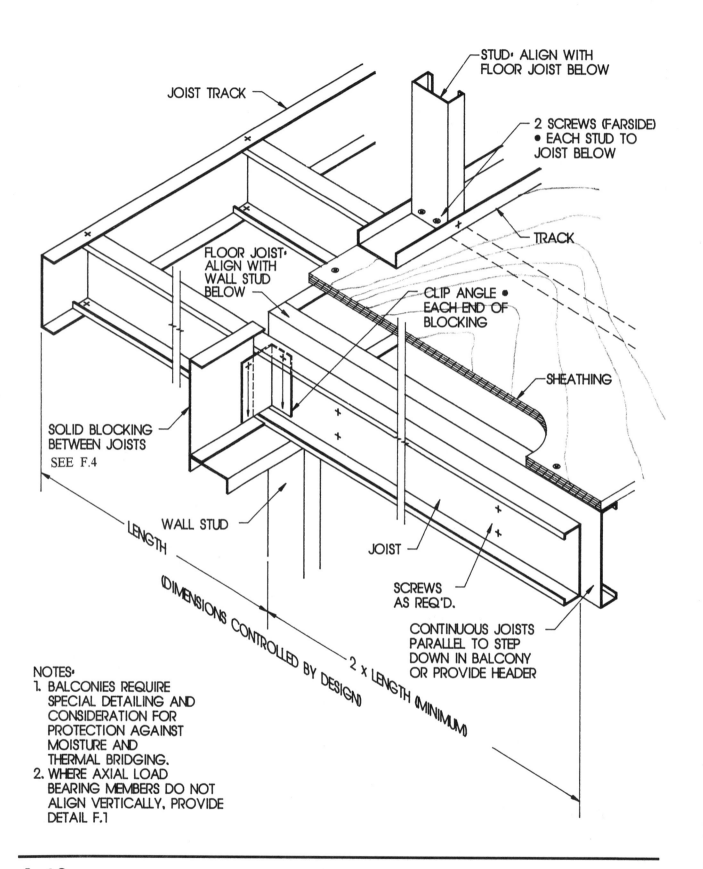

STUD· ALIGN WITH
FLOOR JOIST BELOW

JOIST TRACK

2 SCREWS (FARSIDE)
· EACH STUD TO
JOIST BELOW

TRACK

FLOOR JOIST·
ALIGN WITH
WALL STUD
BELOW

CLIP ANGLE ·
EACH END OF
BLOCKING

SHEATHING

SOLID BLOCKING
BETWEEN JOISTS
SEE F.4

LENGTH

(DIMENSIONS CONTROLLED BY DESIGN)

2 x LENGTH (MINIMUM)

WALL STUD

JOIST

SCREWS
AS REQ'D.

CONTINUOUS JOISTS
PARALLEL TO STEP
DOWN IN BALCONY
OR PROVIDE HEADER

NOTES·
1. BALCONIES REQUIRE
SPECIAL DETAILING AND
CONSIDERATION FOR
PROTECTION AGAINST
MOISTURE AND
THERMAL BRIDGING.
2. WHERE AXIAL LOAD
BEARING MEMBERS DO NOT
ALIGN VERTICALLY, PROVIDE
DETAIL F.1

**A.19**

CANTILEVERED FLOOR AT
STEP DOWN BALCONY FLOOR

# A. FLOOR SYSTEM

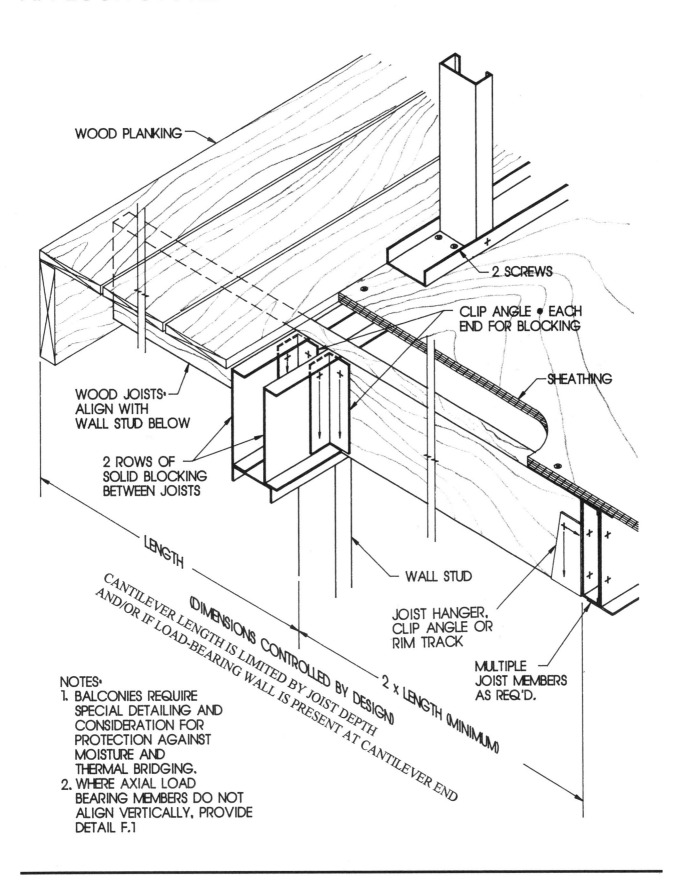

WOOD PLANKING

2 SCREWS

CLIP ANGLE • EACH
END FOR BLOCKING

SHEATHING

WOOD JOISTS•
ALIGN WITH
WALL STUD BELOW

2 ROWS OF
SOLID BLOCKING
BETWEEN JOISTS

WALL STUD

LENGTH

JOIST HANGER,
CLIP ANGLE OR
RIM TRACK

(DIMENSIONS CONTROLLED BY DESIGN)

CANTILEVER LENGTH IS LIMITED BY JOIST DEPTH
AND/OR IF LOAD-BEARING WALL IS PRESENT AT CANTILEVER END

2 x LENGTH (MINIMUM)

MULTIPLE
JOIST MEMBERS
AS REQ'D.

NOTES•
1. BALCONIES REQUIRE
   SPECIAL DETAILING AND
   CONSIDERATION FOR
   PROTECTION AGAINST
   MOISTURE AND
   THERMAL BRIDGING.
2. WHERE AXIAL LOAD
   BEARING MEMBERS DO NOT
   ALIGN VERTICALLY, PROVIDE
   DETAIL F.1

## CANTILEVERED FLOOR AT
## WOOD DECK BALCONY

A.20

# A. FLOOR SYSTEM

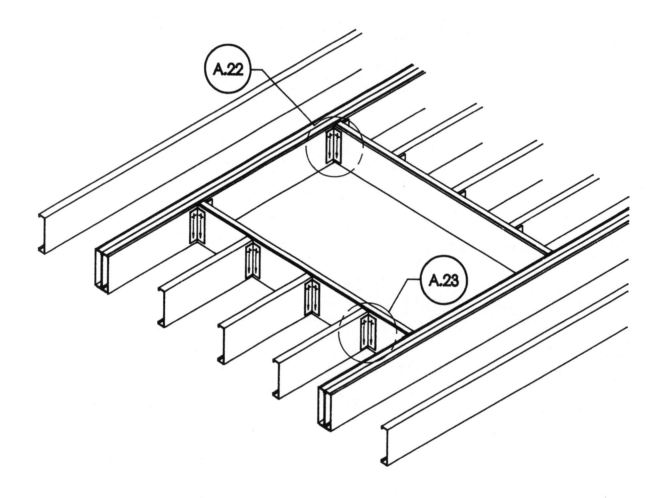

A.22

A.23

# A. FLOOR SYSTEM

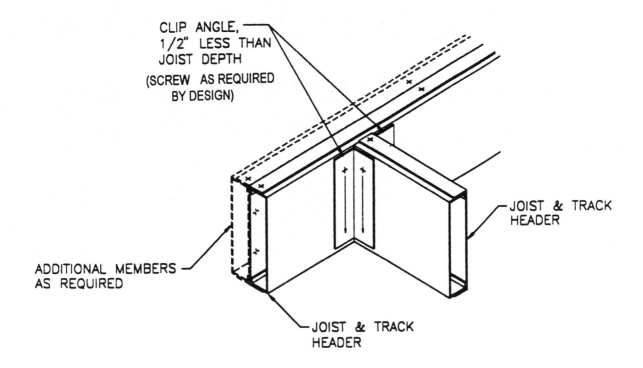

CLIP ANGLE,
1/2" LESS THAN
JOIST DEPTH
(SCREW AS REQUIRED
BY DESIGN)

JOIST & TRACK
HEADER

ADDITIONAL MEMBERS
AS REQUIRED

JOIST & TRACK
HEADER

**JOIST HEADER TO BUILT-UP JOISTS**          **A.22**

# A. FLOOR SYSTEM

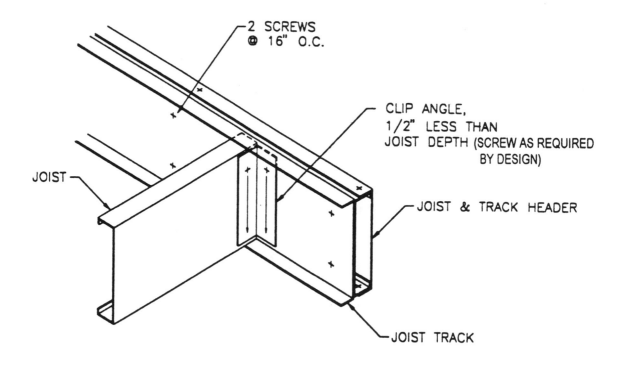

2 SCREWS @ 16" O.C.

CLIP ANGLE, 1/2" LESS THAN JOIST DEPTH (SCREW AS REQUIRED BY DESIGN)

JOIST

JOIST & TRACK HEADER

JOIST TRACK

**A.23**          JOIST HEADER TO FLOOR JOISTS

# A. FLOOR SYSTEM

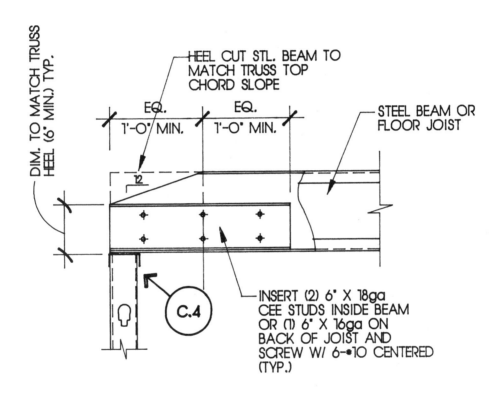

DIM. TO MATCH TRUSS HEEL (6" MIN.) TYP.

HEEL CUT STL. BEAM TO MATCH TRUSS TOP CHORD SLOPE

EQ.
1'-O" MIN.

EQ.
1'-O" MIN.

12

STEEL BEAM OR FLOOR JOIST

C.4

INSERT (2) 6" X 18ga CEE STUDS INSIDE BEAM OR (1) 6" X 16ga ON BACK OF JOIST AND SCREW W/ 6-#10 CENTERED (TYP.)

---

# A. FLOOR SYSTEM

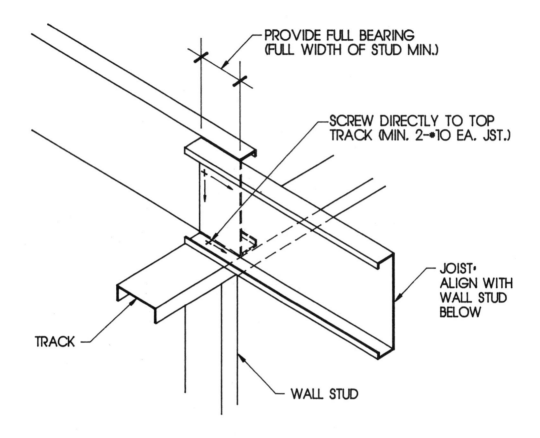

PROVIDE FULL BEARING
(FULL WIDTH OF STUD MIN.)

SCREW DIRECTLY TO TOP
TRACK (MIN. 2-#10 EA. JST.)

JOIST·
ALIGN WITH
WALL STUD
BELOW

TRACK

WALL STUD

NOTES·
1. CONTINUOUS BRIDGING REQ'D. BETWEEN
   EACH JOIST ABOVE WALL - SEE F.6.
   SOLID BLOCKING IN EVERY OTHER SPACE
   MAY BE USED IN LIEU OF BRIDGING.
2. WHEN WALL ABOVE, STUDS MUST ALIGN
   WITH JOISTS.
3. WHERE AXIAL LOAD BEARING MEMBERS DO
   NOT ALIGN VERTICALLY, PROVIDE DETAIL F.1

# B. WALL FRAMING

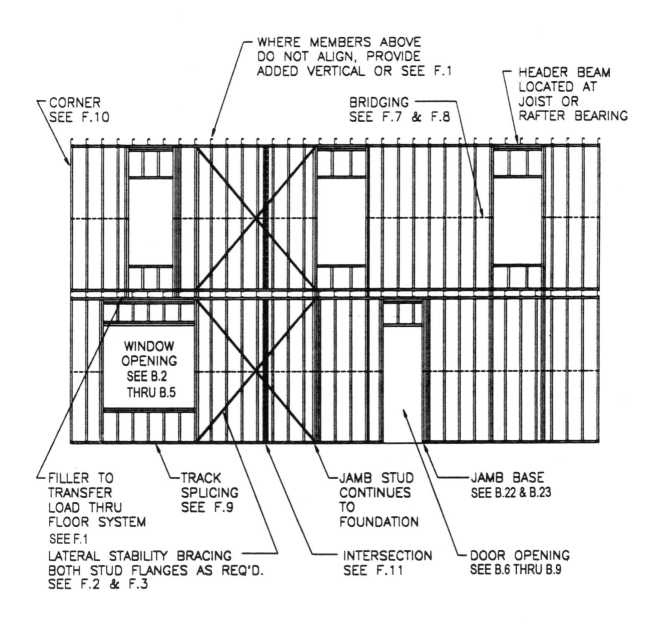

CORNER
SEE F.10

WHERE MEMBERS ABOVE
DO NOT ALIGN, PROVIDE
ADDED VERTICAL OR SEE F.1

BRIDGING
SEE F.7 & F.8

HEADER BEAM
LOCATED AT
JOIST OR
RAFTER BEARING

WINDOW
OPENING
SEE B.2
THRU B.5

FILLER TO
TRANSFER
LOAD THRU
FLOOR SYSTEM
SEE F.1

TRACK
SPLICING
SEE F.9

JAMB STUD
CONTINUES
TO
FOUNDATION

JAMB BASE
SEE B.22 & B.23

LATERAL STABILITY BRACING
BOTH STUD FLANGES AS REQ'D.
SEE F.2 & F.3

INTERSECTION
SEE F.11

DOOR OPENING
SEE B.6 THRU B.9

NOTES:
1. JOISTS ALIGN OVER WALL STUDS (TYP.).

2. JAMB MEMBERS MUST BE CARRIED DOWN
ALL WALLS TO FOUNDATION (TYP.).

3. STUD WEB PENETRATIONS, SEE F.12.

4. HEADERS FOR OPENINGS MAY BE LOCATED
DIRECTLY ABOVE OPENING OR AT JOIST BEARING.
WHEN LOCATED AT WINDOW HEAD, CRIPPLE STUDS
MUST BE TIGHTLY SEATED FOR FULL BEARING.

## TYPICAL WALL FRAMING ELEVATION – 2 STORY    B.1a

# B. WALL FRAMING

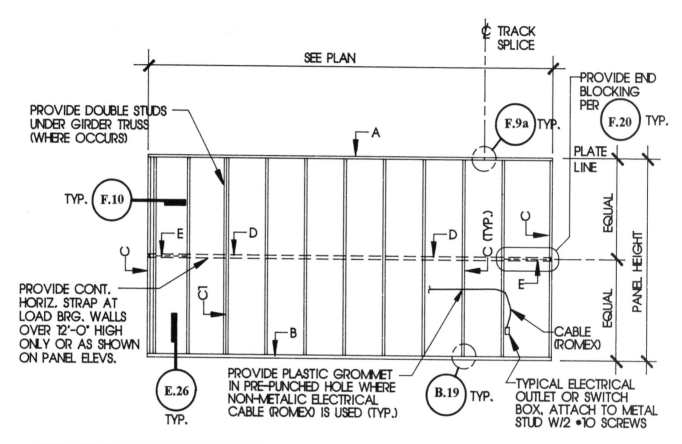

**PROVIDE DOUBLE STUDS UNDER GIRDER TRUSS (WHERE OCCURS)**

**SEE PLAN**

**℄ TRACK SPLICE**

**PROVIDE END BLOCKING PER**  F.20  TYP.

F.9a  TYP.

TYP.  F.10

**PLATE LINE**

EQUAL

EQUAL

PANEL HEIGHT

**PROVIDE CONT. HORIZ. STRAP AT LOAD BRG. WALLS OVER 12'-O" HIGH ONLY OR AS SHOWN ON PANEL ELEVS.**

E.26  TYP.

**PROVIDE PLASTIC GROMMET IN PRE-PUNCHED HOLE WHERE NON-METALIC ELECTRICAL CABLE (ROMEX) IS USED (TYP.)**

B.19  TYP.

**CABLE (ROMEX)**

**TYPICAL ELECTRICAL OUTLET OR SWITCH BOX, ATTACH TO METAL STUD W/2 #10 SCREWS**

| MARK | DESCRIPTION | QTY | SIZE (*) |
|------|-------------|-----|----------|
| A | TOP TRACK | - | 3 1/2" x 20ga |
| B | BOTTOM TRACK | - | 3 1/2" x 20ga |
| C | STUD | - | 3 1/2" x 20ga |
| C1 | DOUBLE STUD | - | (2)3 1/2" x 20ga |
| D | STRAP | - | 2"x16 GA. |
| E | BLOCKING | - | 3 1/2" x 20ga |
|  |  |  |  |
|  |  |  |  |

**SCHEDULE**

NOTES:

\* MEMBER SIZES SHOWN IN THIS DETAIL ARE TYPICAL EXCEPT AS OTHERWISE SHOWN ON THE PLANS OR SPECIFIC PANEL ELEVATIONS.

ALL STUDS SHALL BE SPACED AT 24" O/C EXCEPT AS SHOWN OTHERWISE AND AS NOTED BELOW.

LOAD BEARING STUDS SHALL BE SPACED SO AS TO FALL DIRECTLY UNDER ROOF TRUSSES/RAFTERS OR UNDER FLOOR JOISTS.

**B.1b** TYPICAL WALL FRAMING ELEVATION

# B. WALL FRAMING

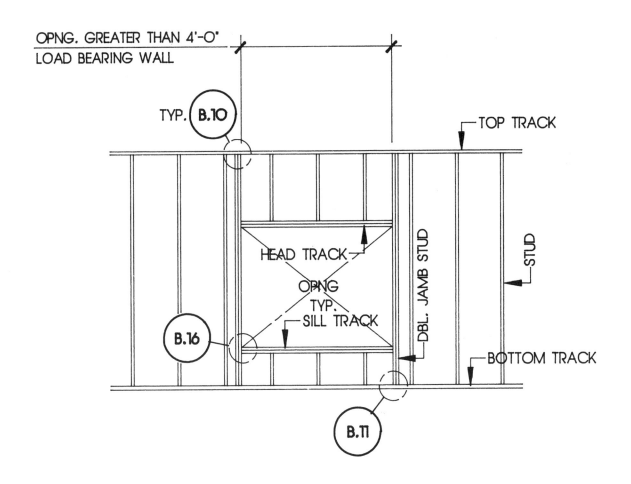

OPNG. GREATER THAN 4'-0"
LOAD BEARING WALL

TYP. **B.10**

TOP TRACK

HEAD TRACK

OPNG
TYP.
SILL TRACK

DBL. JAMB STUD

STUD

**B.16**

BOTTOM TRACK

**B.11**

**WINDOW OPENING GREATER THAN
4 FEET WIDE – NON-LOAD BEARING**

**B.2**

# B. WALL FRAMING

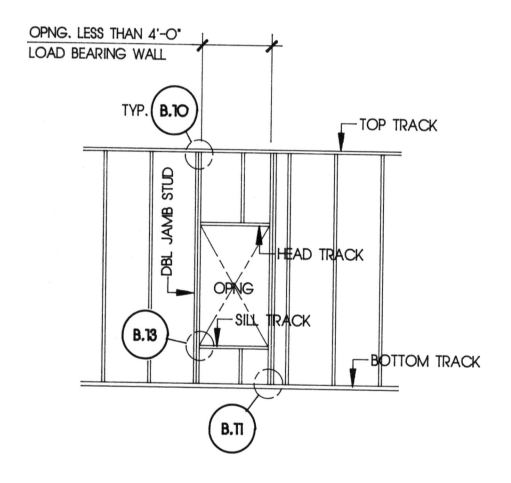

OPNG. LESS THAN 4'-O"
LOAD BEARING WALL

TYP. **B.10**

TOP TRACK

DBL JAMB STUD

HEAD TRACK

OPNG

SILL TRACK

**B.13**

BOTTOM TRACK

**B.11**

**B.3**   WINDOW OPENING LESS THAN
4 FEET WIDE – NON-LOAD BEARING

# B. WALL FRAMING

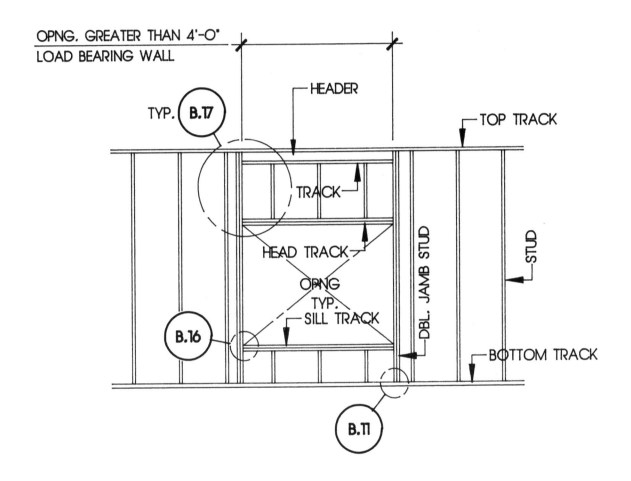

OPNG. GREATER THAN 4'-0"
LOAD BEARING WALL

HEADER

TYP. B.17

TOP TRACK

TRACK

HEAD TRACK

OPNG
TYP.

DBL. JAMB STUD

STUD

SILL TRACK

B.16

B.11

BOTTOM TRACK

**WINDOW OPENING GREATER THAN
4 FEET WIDE – LOAD BEARING**

**B.4**

# B. WALL FRAMING

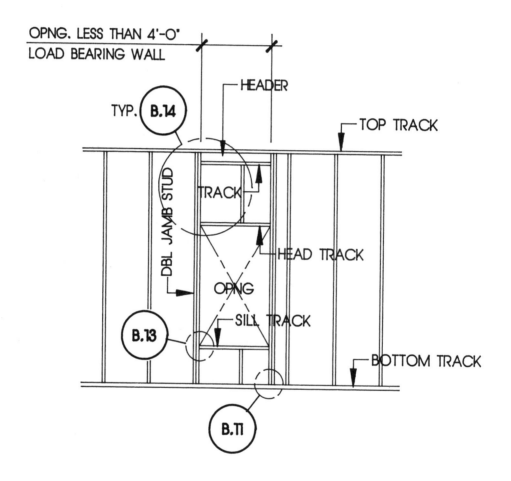

OPNG. LESS THAN 4'-0"
LOAD BEARING WALL

HEADER

TYP. B.14

TOP TRACK

DBL JAMB STUD

TRACK

HEAD TRACK

OPNG

B.13

SILL TRACK

BOTTOM TRACK

B.11

**B.5**

## WINDOW OPENING LESS THAN 4 FEET WIDE LOAD BEARING

# B. WALL FRAMING

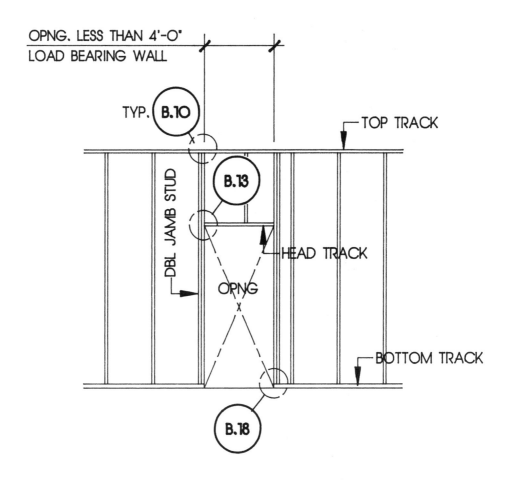

OPNG. LESS THAN 4'-O"
LOAD BEARING WALL

TYP. **B.10**

TOP TRACK

**B.13**

DBL JAMB STUD

HEAD TRACK

OPNG

BOTTOM TRACK

**B.18**

## DOOR OPENING LESS THAN
## 4 FEET WIDE – NON-LOAD BEARING

# B. WALL FRAMING

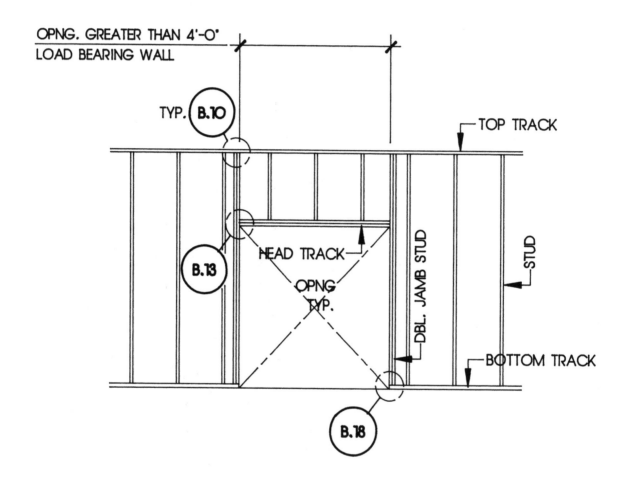

OPNG. GREATER THAN 4'-0"
LOAD BEARING WALL

TYP. B.10

TOP TRACK

B.13

HEAD TRACK

OPNG
TYP.

DBL. JAMB STUD

STUD

BOTTOM TRACK

B.18

**B.7**

**DOOR OPENING GREATER THAN
4 FEET WIDE – NON-LOAD BEARING**

# B. WALL FRAMING

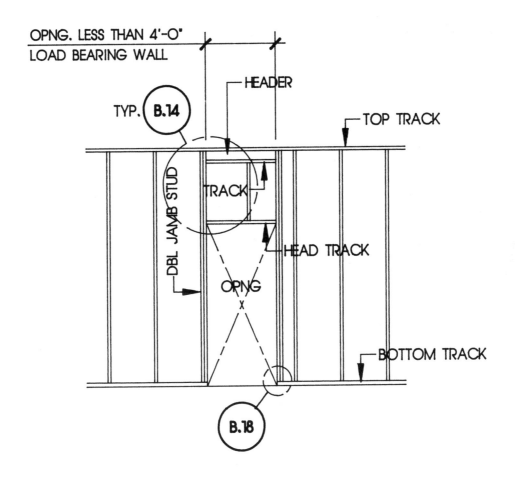

OPNG. LESS THAN 4'-O"
LOAD BEARING WALL

HEADER

TYP. B.14

TOP TRACK

DBL JAMB STUD

TRACK

HEAD TRACK

OPNG

BOTTOM TRACK

B.18

## DOOR OPENING LESS THAN
## 4 FEET WIDE – LOAD BEARING

**B.8**

# B. WALL FRAMING

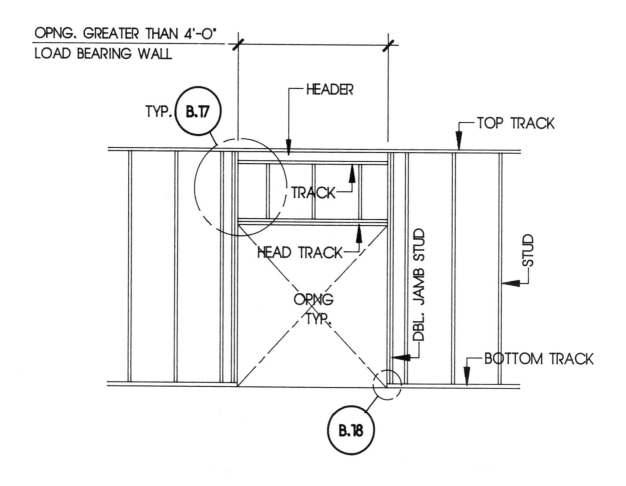

OPNG. GREATER THAN 4'-0"
LOAD BEARING WALL

HEADER

TYP. B.17

TOP TRACK

TRACK

HEAD TRACK

OPNG
TYP.

DBL. JAMB STUD

STUD

BOTTOM TRACK

B.18

**B.9**

## DOOR OPENING GREATER THAN
## 4 FEET WIDE – LOAD BEARING

# B. WALL FRAMING

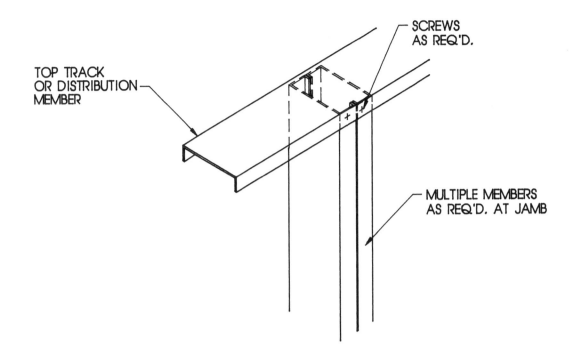

TOP TRACK
OR DISTRIBUTION
MEMBER

SCREWS
AS REQ'D.

MULTIPLE MEMBERS
AS REQ'D. AT JAMB

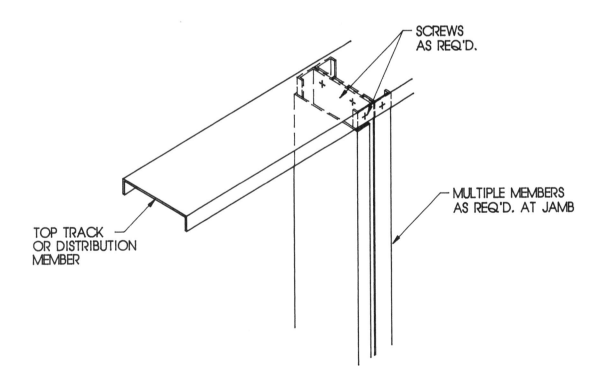

SCREWS
AS REQ'D.

TOP TRACK
OR DISTRIBUTION
MEMBER

MULTIPLE MEMBERS
AS REQ'D. AT JAMB

JAMB AT TOP OF WALL                    **B.10**

# B. WALL FRAMING

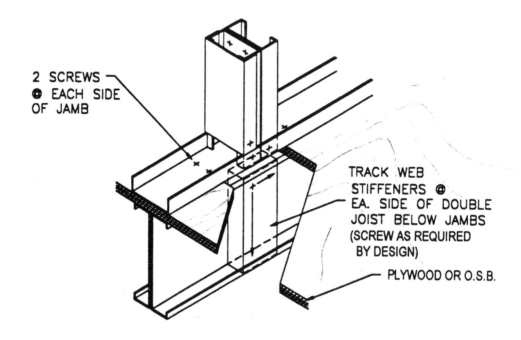

2 SCREWS
@ EACH SIDE
OF JAMB

TRACK WEB
STIFFENERS @
EA. SIDE OF DOUBLE
JOIST BELOW JAMBS
(SCREW AS REQUIRED
BY DESIGN)

PLYWOOD OR O.S.B.

NOTE:
WEB STIFFENERS MAY NOT BE NEEDED DEPENDING UPON
THE PARTICULAR DESIGN REQUIREMENTS.

# B. WALL FRAMING

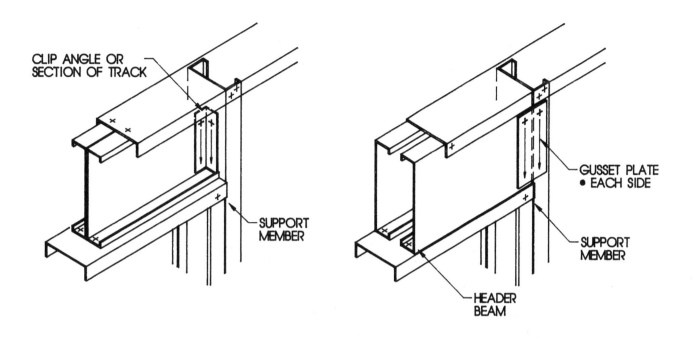

CLIP ANGLE OR
SECTION OF TRACK

SUPPORT
MEMBER

GUSSET PLATE
● EACH SIDE

SUPPORT
MEMBER

HEADER
BEAM

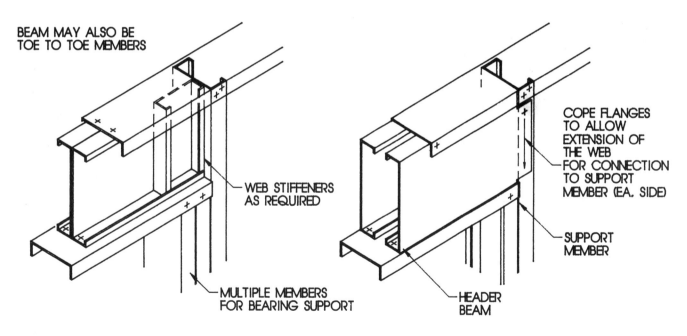

BEAM MAY ALSO BE
TOE TO TOE MEMBERS

WEB STIFFENERS
AS REQUIRED

MULTIPLE MEMBERS
FOR BEARING SUPPORT

COPE FLANGES
TO ALLOW
EXTENSION OF
THE WEB
FOR CONNECTION
TO SUPPORT
MEMBER (EA. SIDE)

SUPPORT
MEMBER

HEADER
BEAM

## HEADER TO JAMB STUD DETAILS

**B.12**

# B. WALL FRAMING

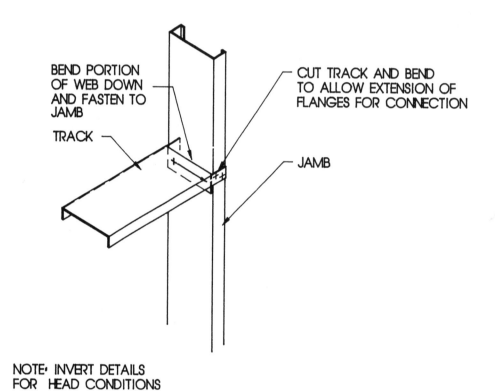

BEND PORTION OF WEB DOWN AND FASTEN TO JAMB

CUT TRACK AND BEND TO ALLOW EXTENSION OF FLANGES FOR CONNECTION

TRACK

JAMB

NOTE· INVERT DETAILS FOR HEAD CONDITIONS

# B. WALL FRAMING

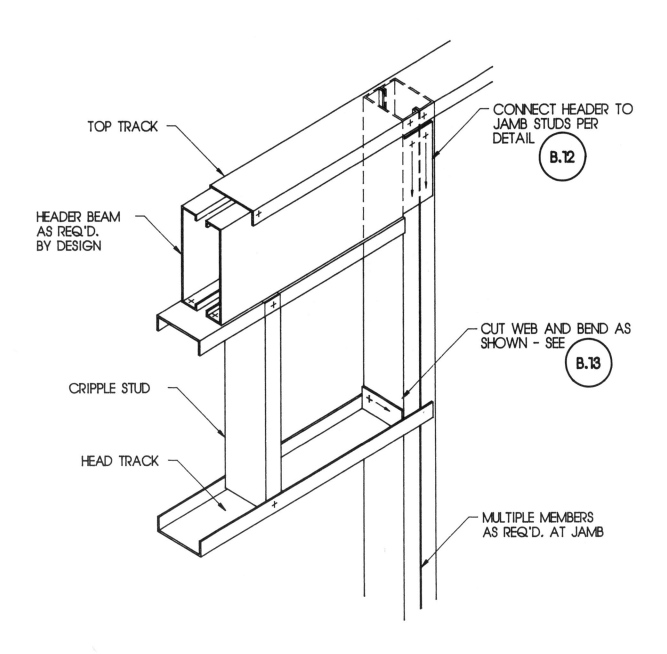

TOP TRACK

HEADER BEAM
AS REQ'D.
BY DESIGN

CRIPPLE STUD

HEAD TRACK

CONNECT HEADER TO
JAMB STUDS PER
DETAIL

**B.12**

CUT WEB AND BEND AS
SHOWN - SEE

**B.13**

MULTIPLE MEMBERS
AS REQ'D. AT JAMB

## OPENING HEAD DETAIL – SINGLE TRACK
## WITH HEADER

**B.14**

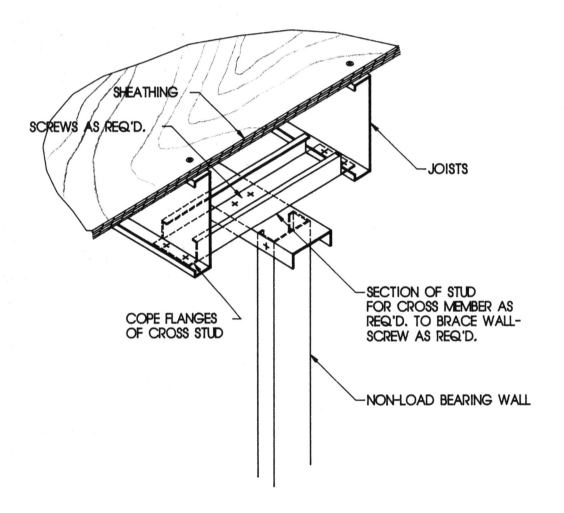

SHEATHING

SCREWS AS REQ'D.

JOISTS

COPE FLANGES
OF CROSS STUD

SECTION OF STUD
FOR CROSS MEMBER AS
REQ'D. TO BRACE WALL-
SCREW AS REQ'D.

NON-LOAD BEARING WALL

TOP OF NON-LOAD BEARING
WALL TO PARALLEL FLOOR JOISTS

# B. WALL FRAMING

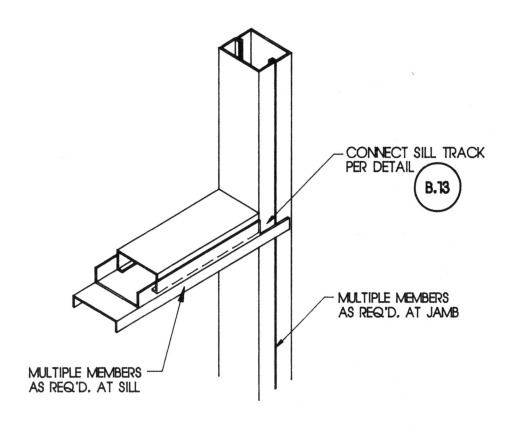

CONNECT SILL TRACK
PER DETAIL

**B.13**

MULTIPLE MEMBERS
AS REQ'D. AT JAMB

MULTIPLE MEMBERS
AS REQ'D. AT SILL

NOTE: INVERT DETAILS
FOR HEAD CONDITIONS

## OPENING SILL DETAIL – BUILT-UP MEMBERS

**B.16**

# B. WALL FRAMING

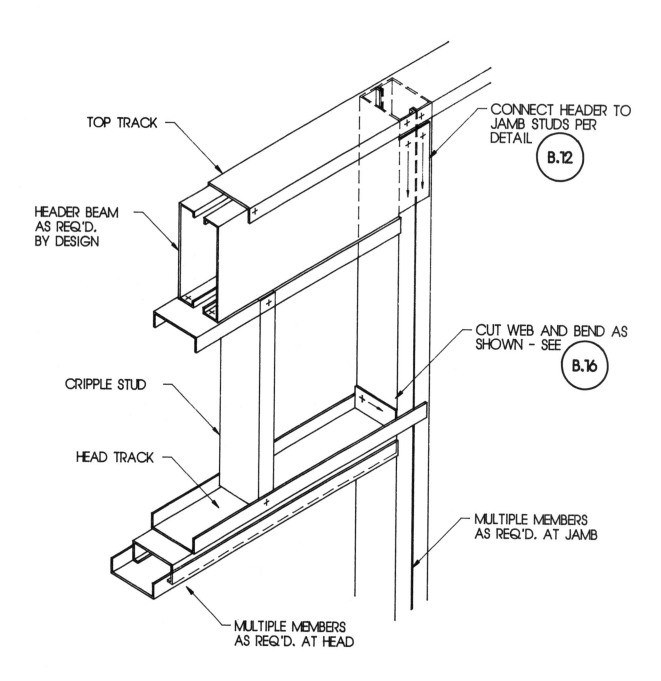

TOP TRACK

HEADER BEAM
AS REQ'D.
BY DESIGN

CONNECT HEADER TO
JAMB STUDS PER
DETAIL
**B.12**

CRIPPLE STUD

CUT WEB AND BEND AS
SHOWN - SEE
**B.16**

HEAD TRACK

MULTIPLE MEMBERS
AS REQ'D. AT JAMB

MULTIPLE MEMBERS
AS REQ'D. AT HEAD

**B.17**   OPENING HEAD DETAIL – LOAD BEARING
JAMB AND HEAD

# B. WALL FRAMING

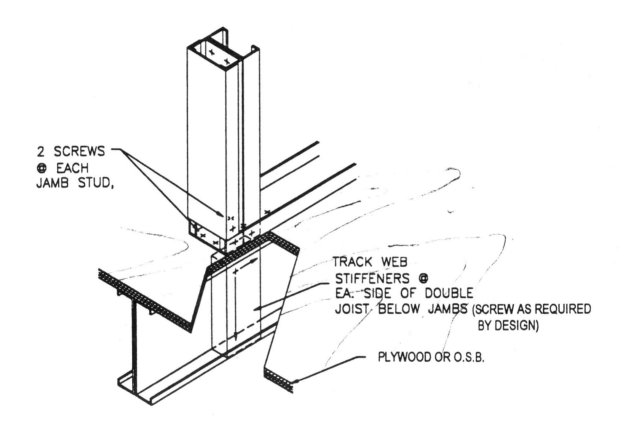

2 SCREWS @ EACH JAMB STUD,

TRACK WEB STIFFENERS @ EA. SIDE OF DOUBLE JOIST BELOW JAMBS (SCREW AS REQUIRED BY DESIGN)

PLYWOOD OR O.S.B.

NOTE:
WEB STIFFENERS MAY NOT BE NEEDED DEPENDING UPON THE PARTICULAR DESIGN REQUIREMENTS.

---

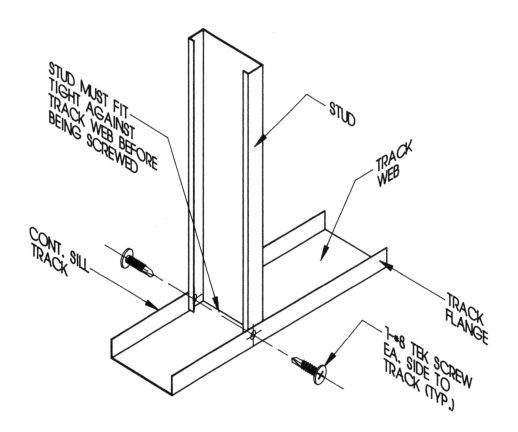

STUD MUST FIT TIGHT AGAINST TRACK WEB BEFORE BEING SCREWED

STUD

TRACK WEB

CONT. SILL TRACK

TRACK FLANGE

1-#8 TEK SCREW EA. SIDE TO TRACK (TYP.)

**B.19**   TYPICAL STUD TO SILL TRACK CONNECTION

# B. WALL FRAMING

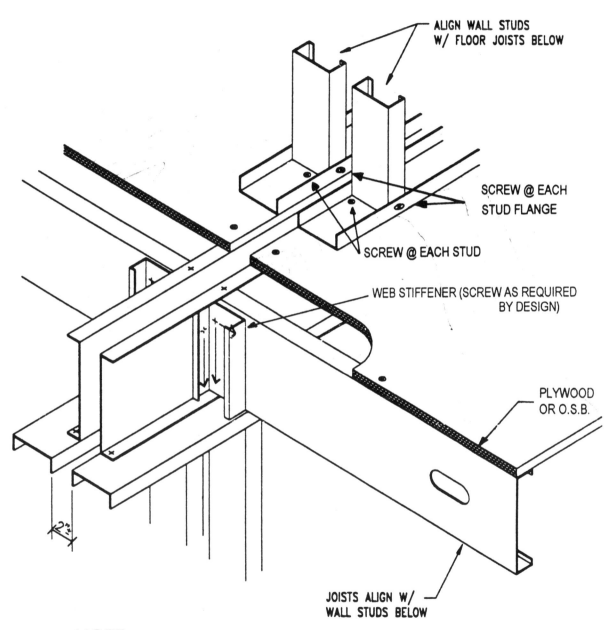

ALIGN WALL STUDS
W/ FLOOR JOISTS BELOW

SCREW @ EACH
STUD FLANGE

SCREW @ EACH STUD

WEB STIFFENER (SCREW AS REQUIRED
BY DESIGN)

PLYWOOD
OR O.S.B.

JOISTS ALIGN W/
WALL STUDS BELOW

NOTE:
IN ORDER TO FACILITATE THE ATTACHMENT OF DRYWALL WHICH
MUST EXTEND TO THE UNDERSIDE OF FLOOR SHEATHING, BLOCKING
MUST BE PROVIDED BETW. EA. JOIST. SEE F.4

---

# B. WALL FRAMING

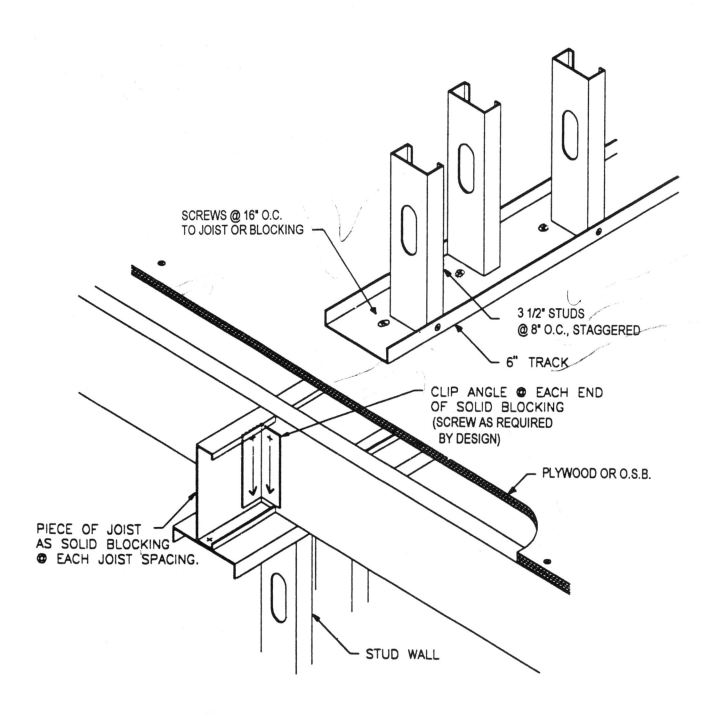

SCREWS @ 16" O.C.
TO JOIST OR BLOCKING

3 1/2" STUDS
@ 8" O.C., STAGGERED

6" TRACK

CLIP ANGLE @ EACH END
OF SOLID BLOCKING
(SCREW AS REQUIRED
BY DESIGN)

PLYWOOD OR O.S.B.

PIECE OF JOIST
AS SOLID BLOCKING
@ EACH JOIST SPACING.

STUD WALL

**B.21**   NON-LOAD BEARING SOUND PARTITION DETAILS

# B. WALL FRAMING

NOTE: DOOR JAMB STUDS MAY BE TURNED FLANGE TO FLANGE
THUS ELIMINATING TRACK SCREWED TO FACE OF JAMB

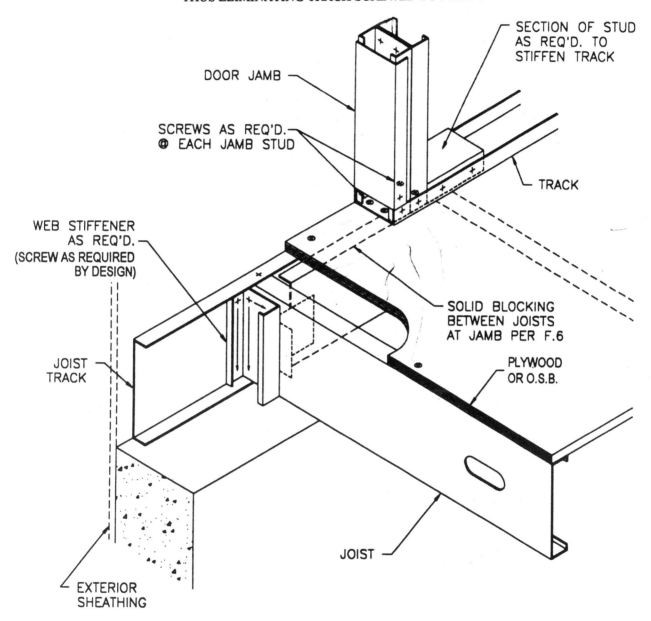

DOOR JAMB

SECTION OF STUD
AS REQ'D. TO
STIFFEN TRACK

SCREWS AS REQ'D.
@ EACH JAMB STUD

TRACK

WEB STIFFENER
AS REQ'D.
(SCREW AS REQUIRED
BY DESIGN)

SOLID BLOCKING
BETWEEN JOISTS
AT JAMB PER F.6

PLYWOOD
OR O.S.B.

JOIST
TRACK

EXTERIOR
SHEATHING

JOIST

---

## DOOR JAMB BASE AT FRAMING

**B.22**

# B. WALL FRAMING

NOTE: DOOR JAMB STUDS MAY BE TURNED FLANGE TO FLANGE
THUS ELIMINATING TRACK SCREWED TO FACE OF JAMB

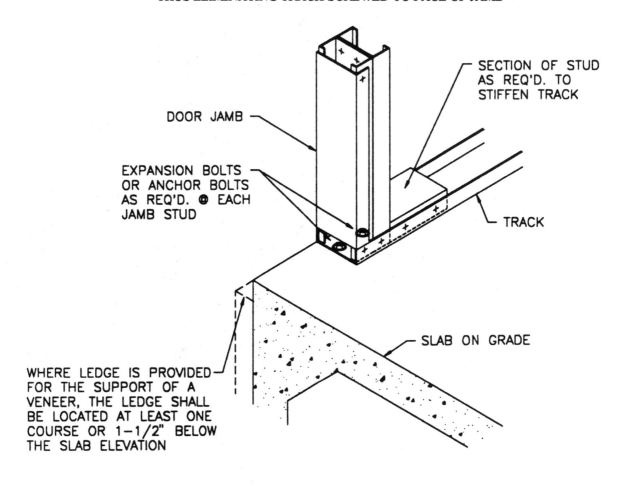

DOOR JAMB

SECTION OF STUD
AS REQ'D. TO
STIFFEN TRACK

EXPANSION BOLTS
OR ANCHOR BOLTS
AS REQ'D. @ EACH
JAMB STUD

TRACK

SLAB ON GRADE

WHERE LEDGE IS PROVIDED
FOR THE SUPPORT OF A
VENEER, THE LEDGE SHALL
BE LOCATED AT LEAST ONE
COURSE OR 1-1/2" BELOW
THE SLAB ELEVATION

**B.23**    DOOR JAMB BASE AT SLAB ON GRADE

FRAMING LAYOUT

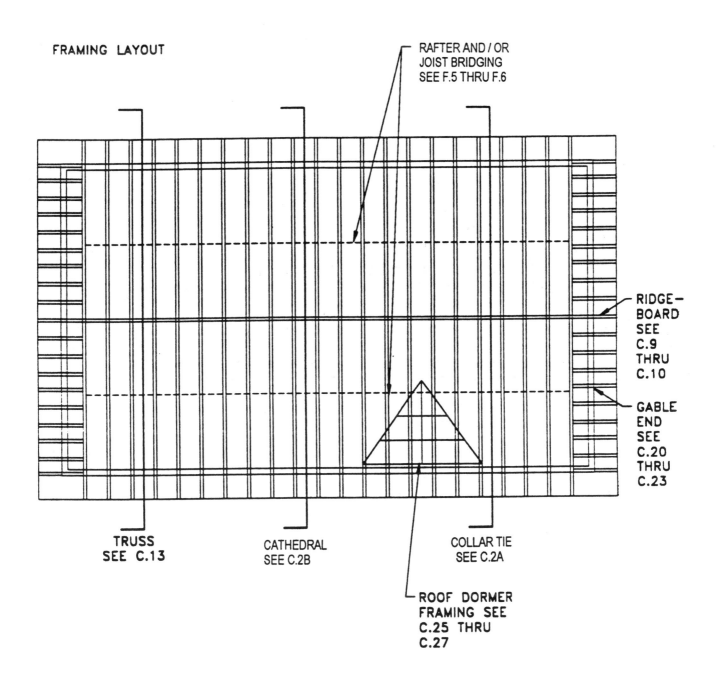

RAFTER AND / OR
JOIST BRIDGING
SEE F.5 THRU F.6

RIDGE—
BOARD
SEE
C.9
THRU
C.10

GABLE
END
SEE
C.20
THRU
C.23

TRUSS
SEE C.13

CATHEDRAL
SEE C.2B

COLLAR TIE
SEE C.2A

ROOF DORMER
FRAMING SEE
C.25 THRU
C.27

# C. CEE CHANNEL ROOF SYSTEM

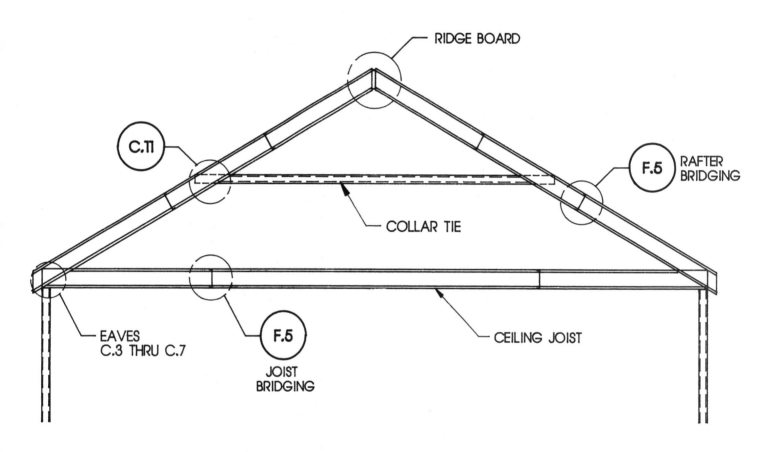

RIDGE BOARD

C.11

F.5 — RAFTER BRIDGING

COLLAR TIE

EAVES
C.3 THRU C.7

F.5

JOIST BRIDGING

CEILING JOIST

**C.2a**    TYPICAL RAFTER FRAMED ROOF SECTION

# C. CEE CHANNEL ROOF SYSTEM

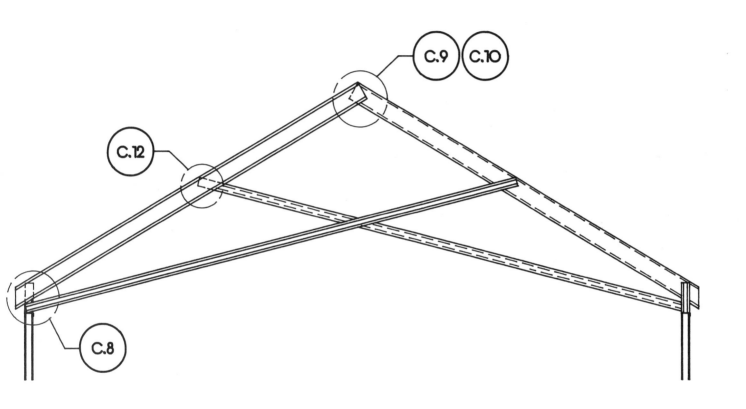

C.9  C.10

C.12

C.8

TYPICAL RAFTER FRAMED
VAULTED / CATHEDRAL CEILING

**C.2b**

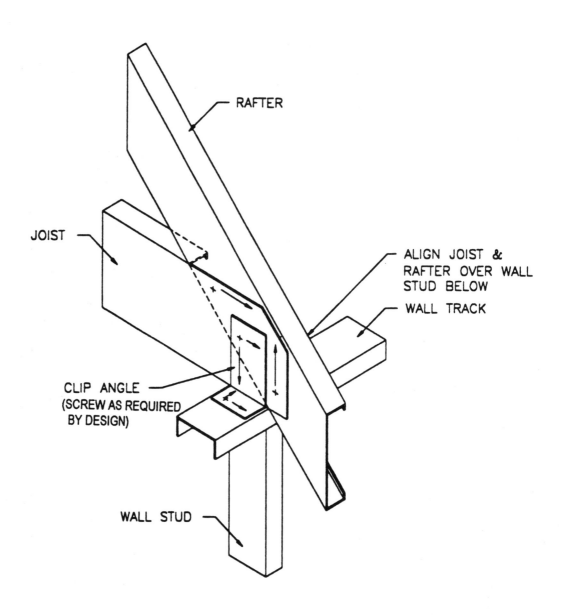

RAFTER

JOIST

ALIGN JOIST &
RAFTER OVER WALL
STUD BELOW

WALL TRACK

CLIP ANGLE
(SCREW AS REQUIRED
BY DESIGN)

WALL STUD

# C. CEE CHANNEL ROOF SYSTEM

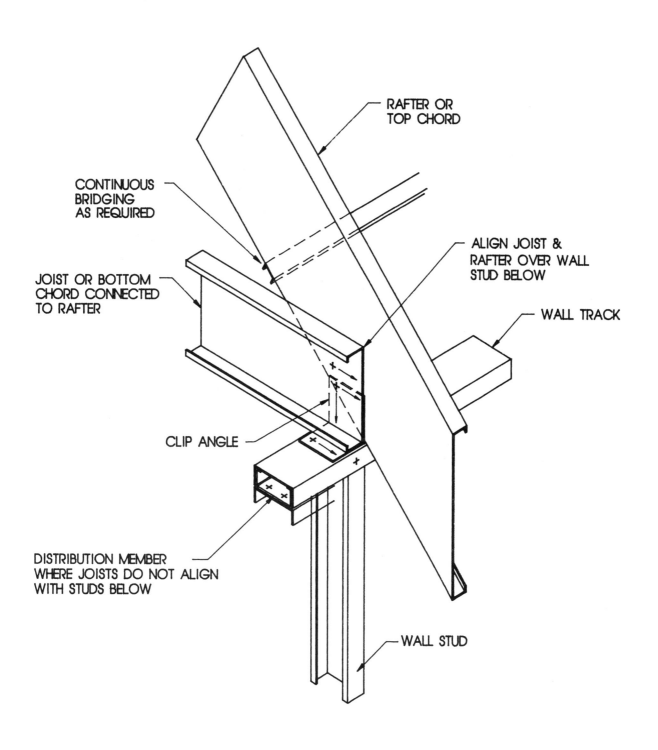

RAFTER OR
TOP CHORD

CONTINUOUS
BRIDGING
AS REQUIRED

ALIGN JOIST &
RAFTER OVER WALL
STUD BELOW

JOIST OR BOTTOM
CHORD CONNECTED
TO RAFTER

WALL TRACK

CLIP ANGLE

DISTRIBUTION MEMBER
WHERE JOISTS DO NOT ALIGN
WITH STUDS BELOW

WALL STUD

---

## RAFTER EAVE DETAIL

# C. CEE CHANNEL ROOF SYSTEM

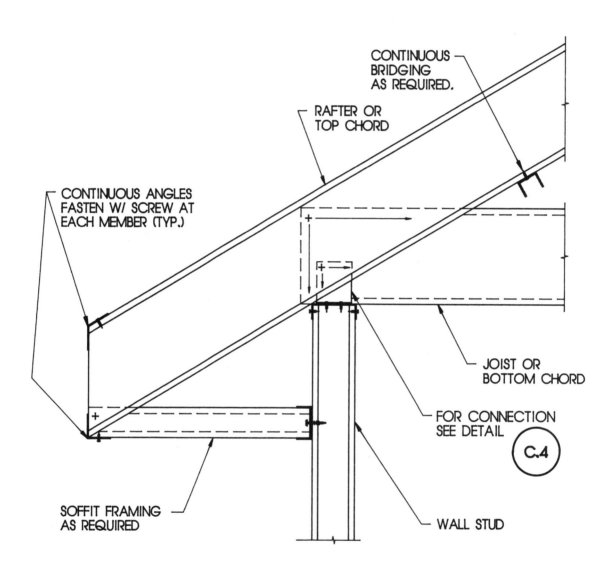

CONTINUOUS BRIDGING AS REQUIRED.

RAFTER OR TOP CHORD

CONTINUOUS ANGLES FASTEN W/ SCREW AT EACH MEMBER (TYP.)

JOIST OR BOTTOM CHORD

FOR CONNECTION SEE DETAIL C.4

SOFFIT FRAMING AS REQUIRED

WALL STUD

**C.5**            RAFTER EAVE DETAIL

# C. CEE CHANNEL ROOF SYSTEM

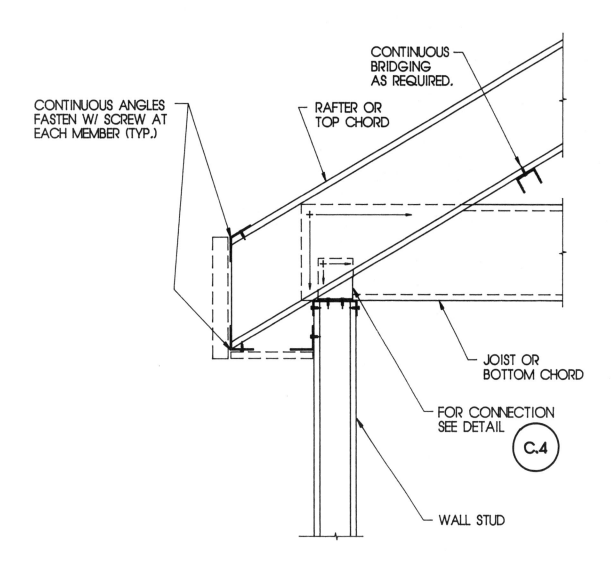

CONTINUOUS
BRIDGING
AS REQUIRED.

RAFTER OR
TOP CHORD

CONTINUOUS ANGLES
FASTEN W/ SCREW AT
EACH MEMBER (TYP.)

JOIST OR
BOTTOM CHORD

FOR CONNECTION
SEE DETAIL

C.4

WALL STUD

---

## RAFTER EAVE DETAIL                    C.6

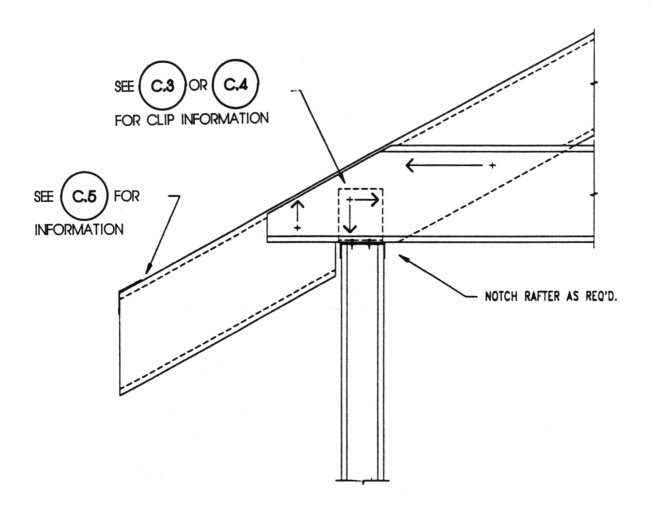

SEE (C.3) OR (C.4)
FOR CLIP INFORMATION

SEE (C.5) FOR
INFORMATION

NOTCH RAFTER AS REQ'D.

# C. CEE CHANNEL ROOF SYSTEM

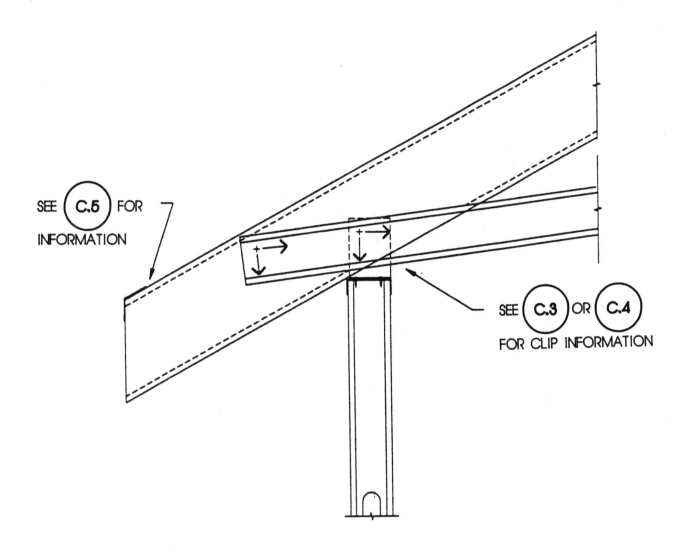

SEE ( C.5 ) FOR

INFORMATION

SEE ( C.3 ) OR ( C.4 )

FOR CLIP INFORMATION

---

## RAFTER EAVE DETAIL

**C.8**

# C. CEE CHANNEL ROOF SYSTEM

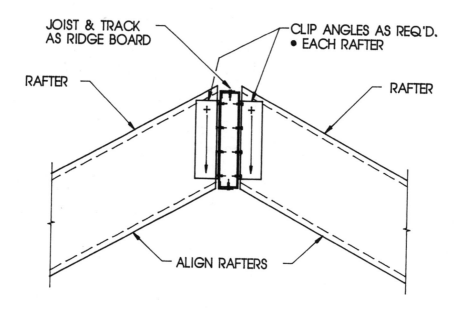

JOIST & TRACK
AS RIDGE BOARD

CLIP ANGLES AS REQ'D.
● EACH RAFTER

RAFTER

RAFTER

ALIGN RAFTERS

---

**C.9**                    RIDGE BOARD DETAIL

# C. CEE CHANNEL ROOF SYSTEM

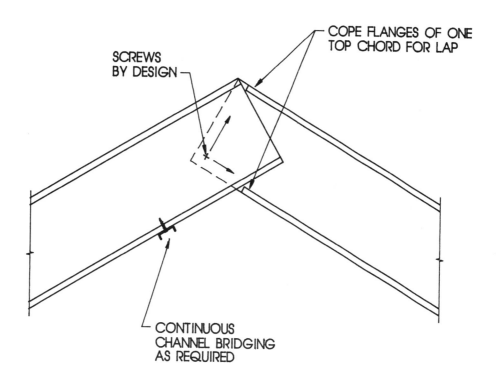

SCREWS
BY DESIGN

COPE FLANGES OF ONE
TOP CHORD FOR LAP

CONTINUOUS
CHANNEL BRIDGING
AS REQUIRED

**RIDGE DETAIL**                                               **C.10**

# C. CEE CHANNEL ROOF SYSTEM

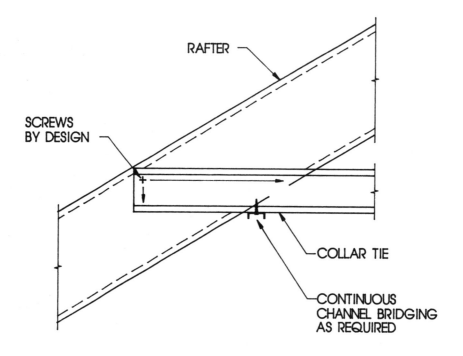

RAFTER

SCREWS
BY DESIGN

COLLAR TIE

CONTINUOUS
CHANNEL BRIDGING
AS REQUIRED

**C.11**          COLLAR TIE AT RAFTER DETAIL

# C. CEE CHANNEL ROOF SYSTEM

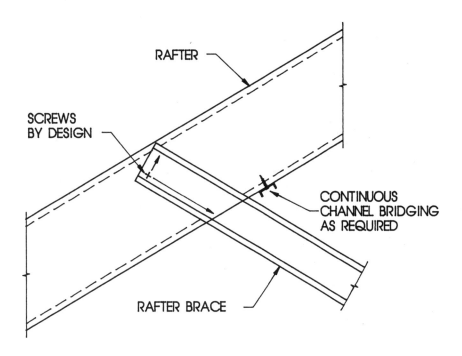

RAFTER

SCREWS
BY DESIGN

CONTINUOUS
CHANNEL BRIDGING
AS REQUIRED

RAFTER BRACE

---

RAFTER TO DIAGONAL BRACE DETAIL          **C.12**

# C. CEE CHANNEL ROOF SYSTEM

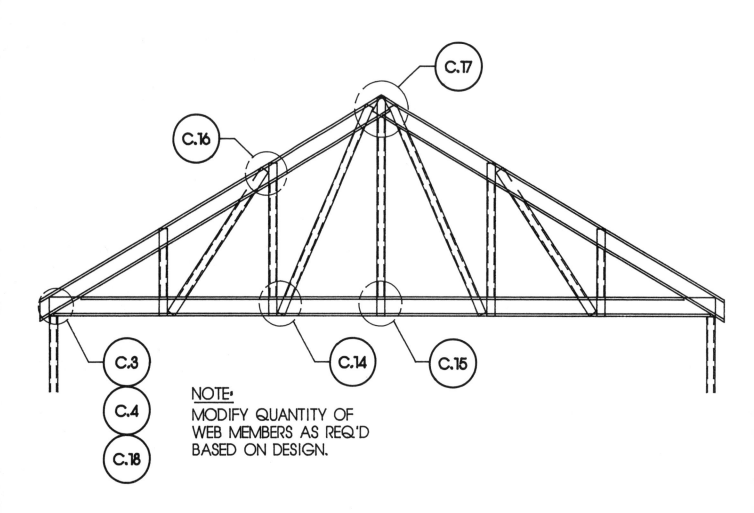

NOTE:
MODIFY QUANTITY OF
WEB MEMBERS AS REQ'D
BASED ON DESIGN.

# C. CEE CHANNEL ROOF SYSTEM

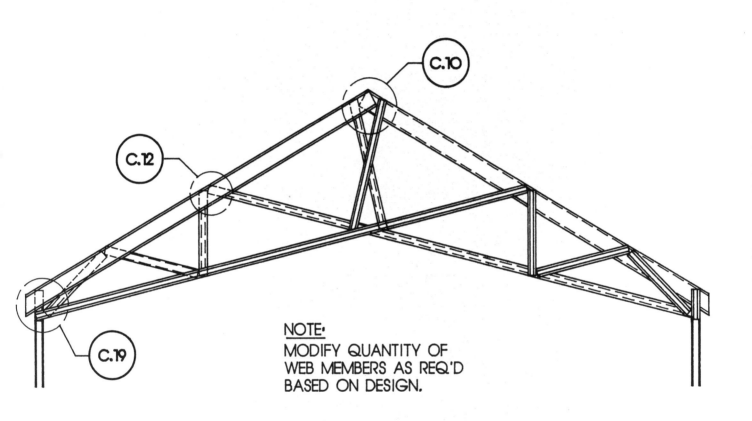

NOTE:
MODIFY QUANTITY OF
WEB MEMBERS AS REQ'D
BASED ON DESIGN.

# C. CEE CHANNEL ROOF SYSTEM

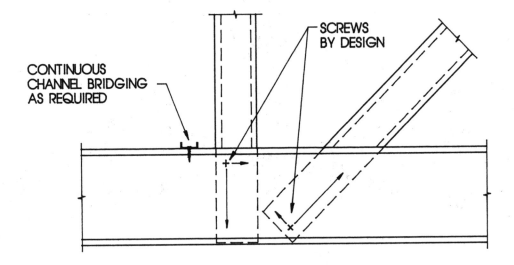

SCREWS
BY DESIGN

CONTINUOUS
CHANNEL BRIDGING
AS REQUIRED

# C. CEE CHANNEL ROOF SYSTEM

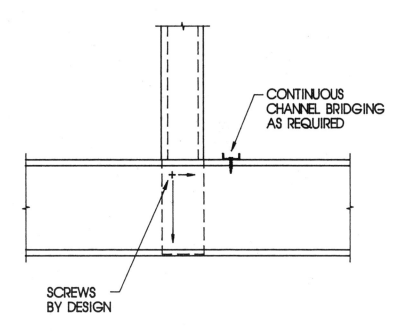

CONTINUOUS
CHANNEL BRIDGING
AS REQUIRED

SCREWS
BY DESIGN

# C. CEE CHANNEL ROOF SYSTEM

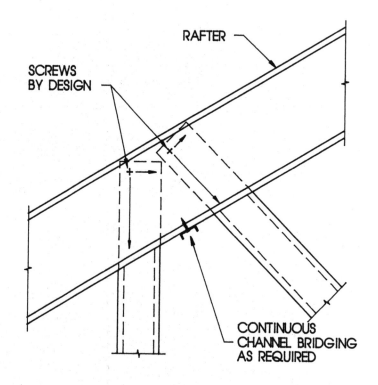

SCREWS
BY DESIGN

RAFTER

CONTINUOUS
CHANNEL BRIDGING
AS REQUIRED

# C. CEE CHANNEL ROOF SYSTEM

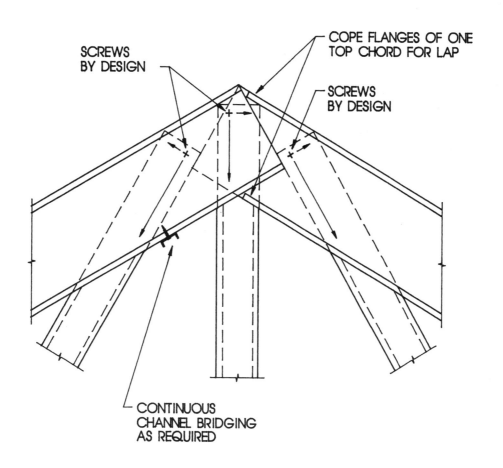

COPE FLANGES OF ONE
TOP CHORD FOR LAP

SCREWS
BY DESIGN

SCREWS
BY DESIGN

CONTINUOUS
CHANNEL BRIDGING
AS REQUIRED

# C. CEE CHANNEL ROOF SYSTEM

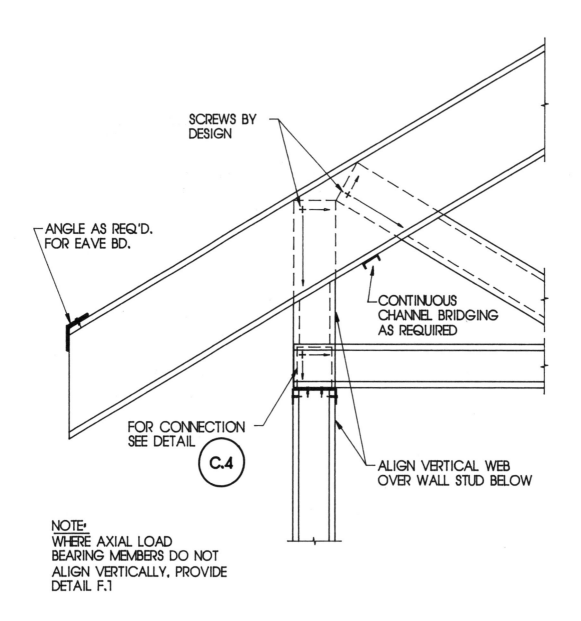

SCREWS BY
DESIGN

ANGLE AS REQ'D.
FOR EAVE BD.

CONTINUOUS
CHANNEL BRIDGING
AS REQUIRED

FOR CONNECTION
SEE DETAIL

C.4

ALIGN VERTICAL WEB
OVER WALL STUD BELOW

NOTE:
WHERE AXIAL LOAD
BEARING MEMBERS DO NOT
ALIGN VERTICALLY, PROVIDE
DETAIL F.1

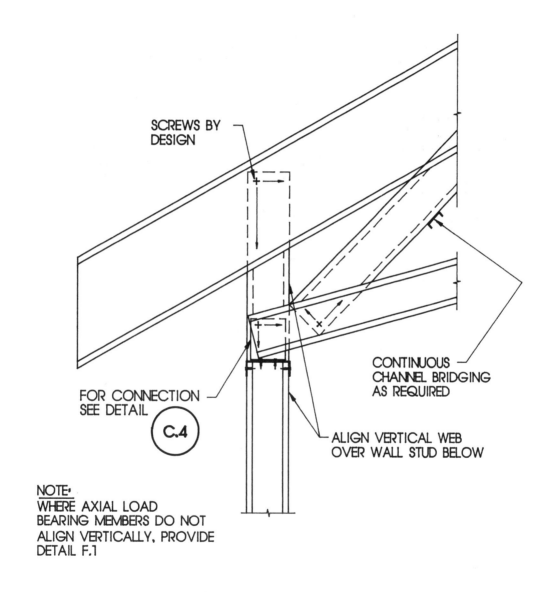

SCREWS BY
DESIGN

FOR CONNECTION
SEE DETAIL
C.4

CONTINUOUS
CHANNEL BRIDGING
AS REQUIRED

ALIGN VERTICAL WEB
OVER WALL STUD BELOW

NOTE:
WHERE AXIAL LOAD
BEARING MEMBERS DO NOT
ALIGN VERTICALLY, PROVIDE
DETAIL F.1

**SCISSORS TRUSS END AT EXTERIOR WALL**

**C.19**

# C. CEE CHANNEL ROOF SYSTEM

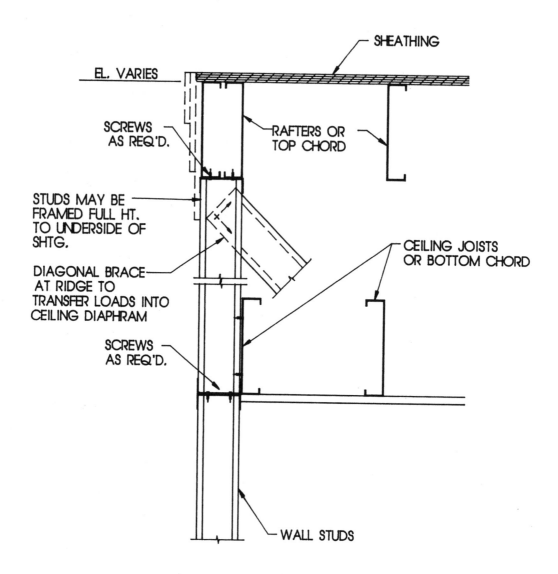

SHEATHING

EL. VARIES

SCREWS
AS REQ'D.

RAFTERS OR
TOP CHORD

STUDS MAY BE
FRAMED FULL HT.
TO UNDERSIDE OF
SHTG.

DIAGONAL BRACE
AT RIDGE TO
TRANSFER LOADS INTO
CEILING DIAPHRAM

CEILING JOISTS
OR BOTTOM CHORD

SCREWS
AS REQ'D.

WALL STUDS

NOTE·
PROVIDE BRIDGING PER F.6
AT CEILING JOISTS AND RAFTERS.

**C.20**          GABLE ROOF END DETAIL

# C. CEE CHANNEL ROOF SYSTEM

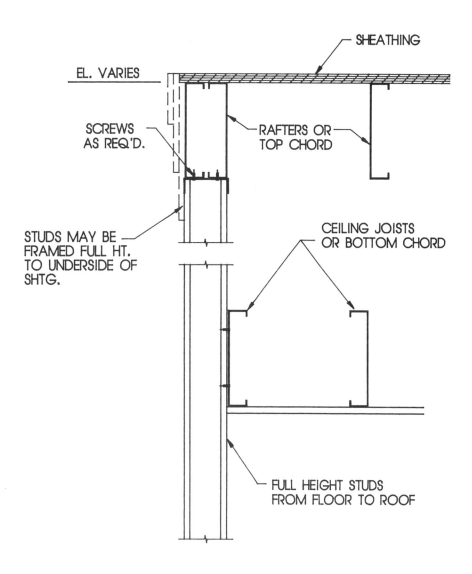

SHEATHING

EL. VARIES

SCREWS
AS REQ'D.

RAFTERS OR
TOP CHORD

STUDS MAY BE
FRAMED FULL HT.
TO UNDERSIDE OF
SHTG.

CEILING JOISTS
OR BOTTOM CHORD

FULL HEIGHT STUDS
FROM FLOOR TO ROOF

NOTE·
PROVIDE BRIDGING PER F.6

## GABLE ROOF END DETAIL                    C.21

# C. CEE CHANNEL ROOF SYSTEM

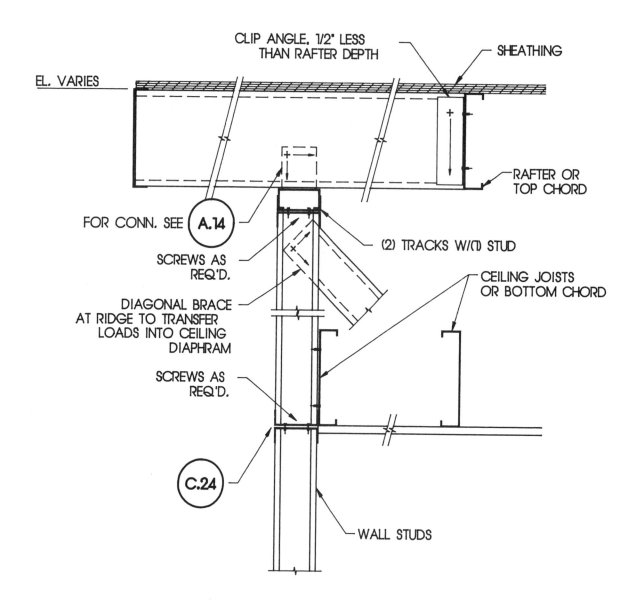

CLIP ANGLE, 1/2" LESS
THAN RAFTER DEPTH

SHEATHING

EL. VARIES

RAFTER OR
TOP CHORD

FOR CONN. SEE A.14

(2) TRACKS W/(1) STUD

SCREWS AS
REQ'D.

CEILING JOISTS
OR BOTTOM CHORD

DIAGONAL BRACE
AT RIDGE TO TRANSFER
LOADS INTO CEILING
DIAPHRAM

SCREWS AS
REQ'D.

C.24

WALL STUDS

NOTES:
1. PROVIDE BRIDGING PER F.6
   AT CEILING JOISTS AND
   ROOF RAFTERS.
2. PROVIDE CONTINUOUS BRIDGING
   BETWEEN RAFTERS AT WALL PER F.6

**C.22**          GABLE ROOF END DETAIL

# C. CEE CHANNEL ROOF SYSTEM

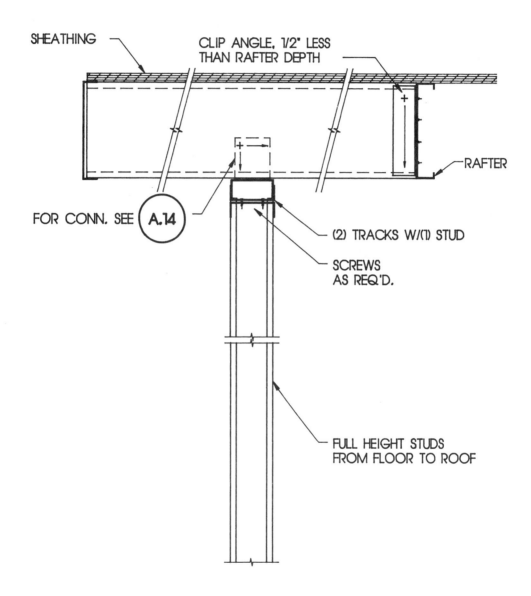

SHEATHING

CLIP ANGLE, 1/2" LESS
THAN RAFTER DEPTH

RAFTER

FOR CONN. SEE **A.14**

(2) TRACKS W/(1) STUD

SCREWS
AS REQ'D.

FULL HEIGHT STUDS
FROM FLOOR TO ROOF

NOTES:
1. PROVIDE BRIDGING PER F.6

2. PROVIDE CONTINUOUS BRIDGING
   BETWEEN RAFTERS AT WALL PER F.6

---

BALLOON FRAMED GABLE ROOF END DETAIL **C.23**

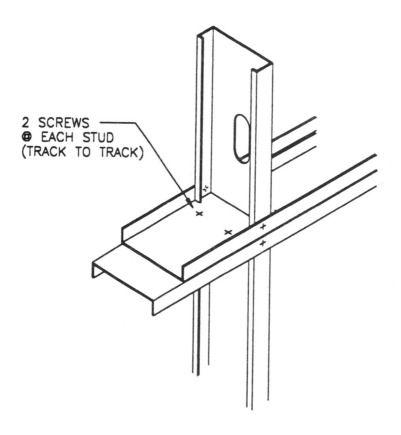

2 SCREWS
@ EACH STUD
(TRACK TO TRACK)

NOTE:
JOINT MUST BE BRACED DIAGONALLY OR HORIZONTALLY
TO THE NEAREST ROOF OR FLOOR FRAMING MEMBER.

# C. CEE CHANNEL ROOF SYSTEM

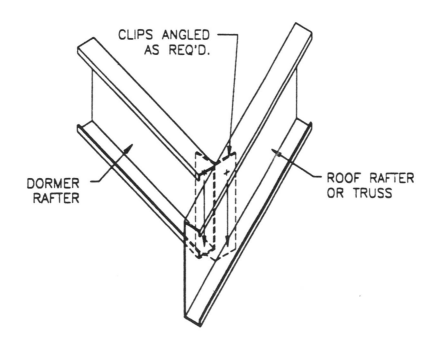

CLIPS ANGLED
AS REQ'D.

DORMER
RAFTER

ROOF RAFTER
OR TRUSS

SUPPORTED MEMBER MAY BE CONNECTED BY CUTTING
FLANGES – BENDING WEB TO DESIRED ANGLE & FASTENING
DIRECTLY WITH SCREWS AS DESIGNED.

# C. CEE CHANNEL ROOF SYSTEM

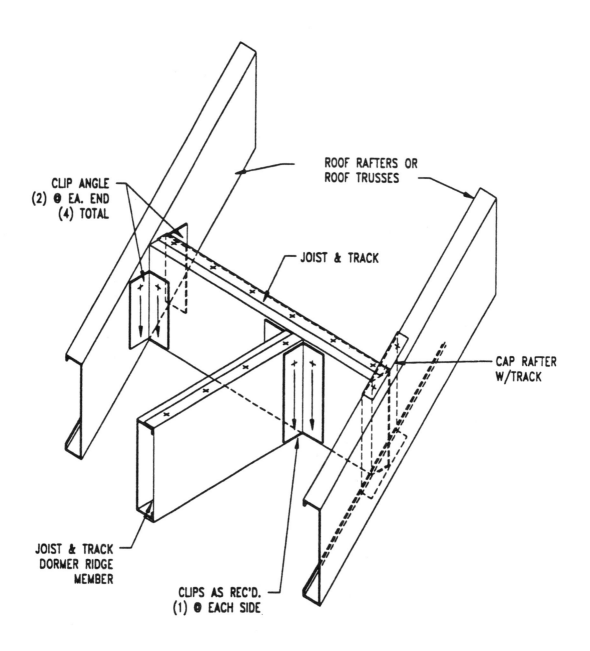

CLIP ANGLE
(2) @ EA. END
(4) TOTAL

ROOF RAFTERS OR
ROOF TRUSSES

JOIST & TRACK

CAP RAFTER
W/TRACK

JOIST & TRACK
DORMER RIDGE
MEMBER

CLIPS AS REC'D.
(1) @ EACH SIDE

**C.26**     DORMER RIDGE AT MAIN ROOF DETAIL

# C. CEE CHANNEL ROOF SYSTEM

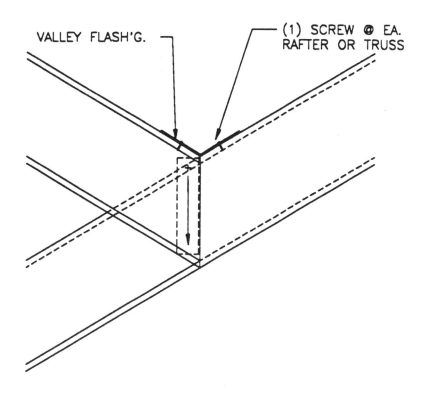

VALLEY FLASH'G.

(1) SCREW @ EA.
RAFTER OR TRUSS

---

## VALLEY FLASHING DETAIL

# C. CEE CHANNEL ROOF SYSTEM

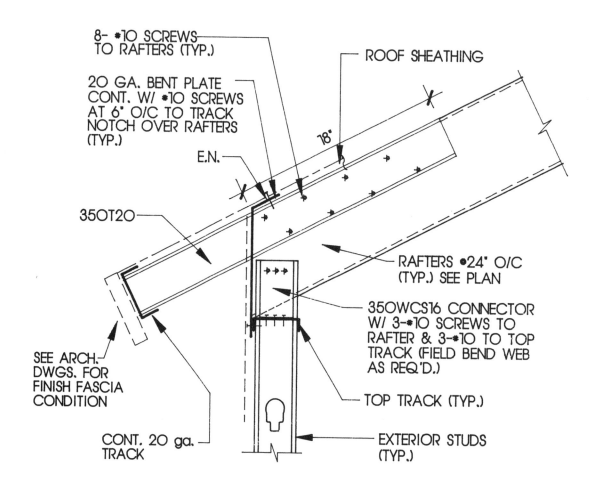

8- #10 SCREWS TO RAFTERS (TYP.)

20 GA. BENT PLATE CONT. W/ #10 SCREWS AT 6" O/C TO TRACK NOTCH OVER RAFTERS (TYP.)

E.N.

350T20

ROOF SHEATHING

18"

RAFTERS ●24" O/C (TYP.) SEE PLAN

350WCS16 CONNECTOR W/ 3-#10 SCREWS TO RAFTER & 3-#10 TO TOP TRACK (FIELD BEND WEB AS REQ'D.)

TOP TRACK (TYP.)

EXTERIOR STUDS (TYP.)

SEE ARCH. DWGS. FOR FINISH FASCIA CONDITION

CONT. 20 ga. TRACK

# C. CEE CHANNEL ROOF SYSTEM

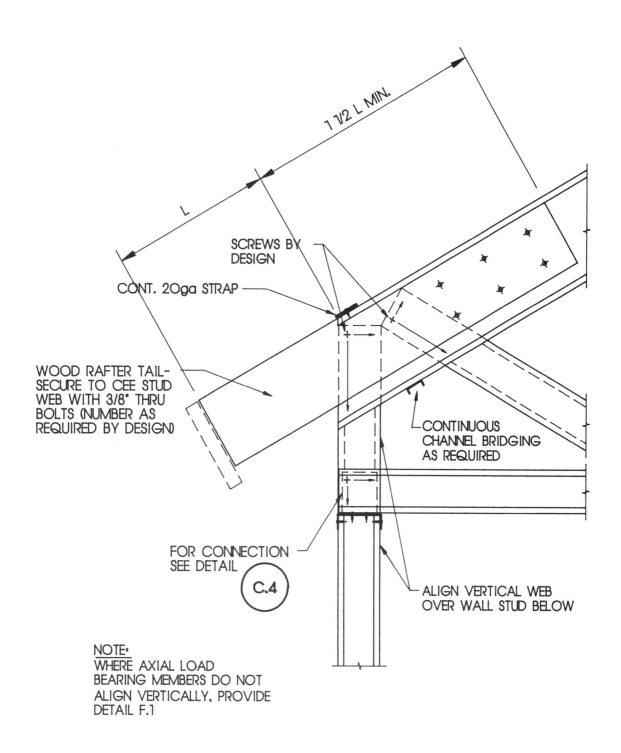

1 1/2 L MIN.

L

SCREWS BY
DESIGN

CONT. 20ga STRAP

WOOD RAFTER TAIL-
SECURE TO CEE STUD
WEB WITH 3/8" THRU
BOLTS (NUMBER AS
REQUIRED BY DESIGN)

CONTINUOUS
CHANNEL BRIDGING
AS REQUIRED

FOR CONNECTION
SEE DETAIL

C.4

ALIGN VERTICAL WEB
OVER WALL STUD BELOW

NOTE:
WHERE AXIAL LOAD
BEARING MEMBERS DO NOT
ALIGN VERTICALLY, PROVIDE
DETAIL F.1

---

WOOD TAIL CONNECTION TO TRUSS　　　　**C.29**

# D. GUS TRUSS™ ROOF SYSTEM

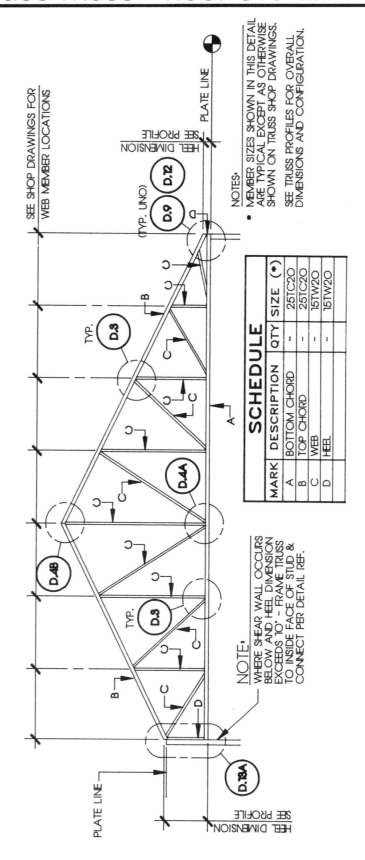

**SCHEDULE**

| MARK | DESCRIPTION | QTY | SIZE (*) |
|------|-------------|-----|----------|
| A | BOTTOM CHORD | – | 25TC2O |
| B | TOP CHORD | – | 25TC2O |
| C | WEB | – | 15TW2O |
| D | HEEL | – | 15TW2O |

SEE SHOP DRAWINGS FOR WEB MEMBER LOCATIONS

HEEL DIMENSION — SEE PROFILE

PLATE LINE

NOTES:
- MEMBER SIZES SHOWN IN THIS DETAIL ARE TYPICAL EXCEPT AS OTHERWISE SHOWN ON TRUSS SHOP DRAWINGS.

SEE TRUSS PROFILES FOR OVERALL DIMENSIONS AND CONFIGURATION.

(TYP. UNO)

D.12

D.9

TYP.

D.3

D.4A

D.4B

D.3

NOTE:
WHERE SHEAR WALL OCCURS BELOW AND HEEL DIMENSION EXCEEDS 10' - FRAME TRUSS TO INSIDE FACE OF STUD & CONNECT PER DETAIL REF.

D.13A

PLATE LINE

HEEL DIMENSION — SEE PROFILE

---

## TYPICAL GUSS TRUSS™ ELEVATION

**D.1a**

# D. GUS TRUSS™ ROOF SYSTEM

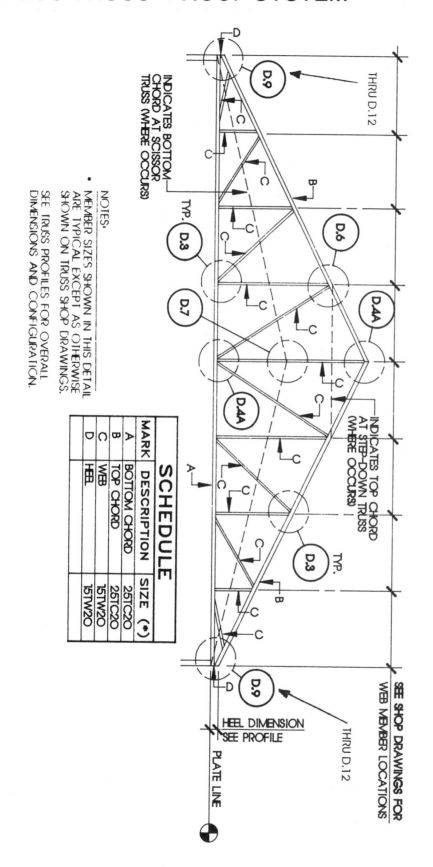

**SCHEDULE**

| MARK | DESCRIPTION | SIZE (*) |
|------|-------------|----------|
| A | BOTTOM CHORD | 25TC2O |
| B | TOP CHORD | 25TC2O |
| C | WEB | 15TW2O |
| D | HEEL | 15TW2O |

NOTES:

• MEMBER SIZES SHOWN IN THIS DETAIL ARE TYPICAL EXCEPT AS OTHERWISE SHOWN ON TRUSS SHOP DRAWINGS.

• SEE TRUSS PROFILES FOR OVERALL DIMENSIONS AND CONFIGURATION.

INDICATES BOTTOM CHORD AT SCISSOR TRUSS (WHERE OCCURS)

INDICATES TOP CHORD AT STEP-DOWN TRUSS (WHERE OCCURS)

THRU D.12

SEE SHOP DRAWINGS FOR WEB MEMBER LOCATIONS

THRU D.12

HEEL DIMENSION SEE PROFILE

PLATE LINE

**D.1b**          TYPICAL GUSS TRUSS™ ELEVATION

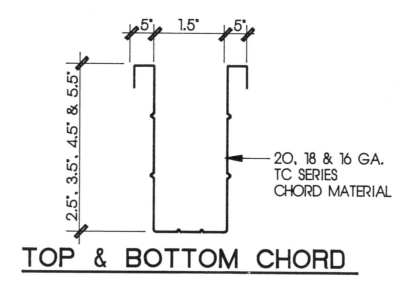

2O, 18 & 16 GA.
TC SERIES
CHORD MATERIAL

## TOP & BOTTOM CHORD

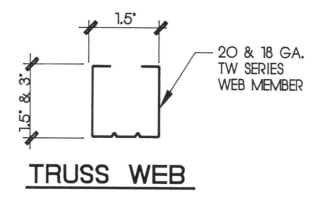

2O & 18 GA.
TW SERIES
WEB MEMBER

## TRUSS WEB

# D. GUS TRUSS™ ROOF SYSTEM

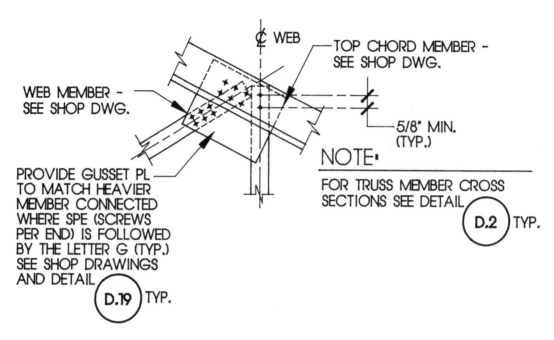

WEB MEMBER -
SEE SHOP DWG.

℄ WEB

TOP CHORD MEMBER -
SEE SHOP DWG.

5/8" MIN.
(TYP.)

PROVIDE GUSSET PL
TO MATCH HEAVIER
MEMBER CONNECTED
WHERE SPE (SCREWS
PER END) IS FOLLOWED
BY THE LETTER G (TYP.)
SEE SHOP DRAWINGS
AND DETAIL ( D.19 ) TYP.

NOTE:

FOR TRUSS MEMBER CROSS
SECTIONS SEE DETAIL ( D.2 ) TYP.

## DETAIL AT TOP CHORD

**NOTE:** GUSSET PLATE MAY NOT BE REQUIRED IF CALCULATED
NUMBER OF SCREWS CAN BE DIRECTLY APPLIED TO
ALL JOINED WEBS THROUGH CHORD MEMBER.

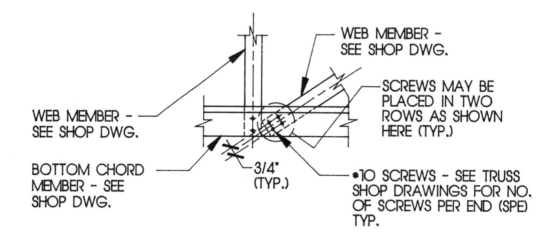

WEB MEMBER -
SEE SHOP DWG.

WEB MEMBER -
SEE SHOP DWG.

SCREWS MAY BE
PLACED IN TWO
ROWS AS SHOWN
HERE (TYP.)

BOTTOM CHORD
MEMBER - SEE
SHOP DWG.

3/4"
(TYP.)

*10 SCREWS - SEE TRUSS
SHOP DRAWINGS FOR NO.
OF SCREWS PER END (SPE)
TYP.

## DETAIL AT BOTTOM CHORD

---

**D.3**          TRUSS WEB CONNECTION DETAIL

# D. GUS TRUSS™ ROOF SYSTEM

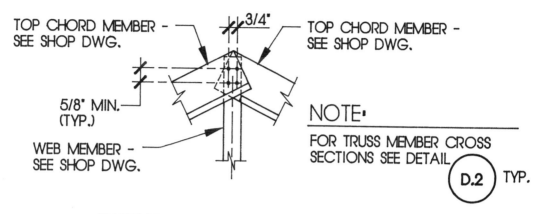

TOP CHORD MEMBER - SEE SHOP DWG.

3/4"

TOP CHORD MEMBER - SEE SHOP DWG.

5/8" MIN. (TYP.)

WEB MEMBER - SEE SHOP DWG.

**NOTE:**

FOR TRUSS MEMBER CROSS SECTIONS SEE DETAIL ( D.2 ) TYP.

## DETAIL AT TOP CHORD

**NOTE: GUSSET PLATE MAY NOT BE REQUIRED IF CALCULATED NUMBER OF SCREWS CAN BE DIRECTLY APPLIED TO ALL JOINED WEBS THROUGH CHORD MEMBER.**

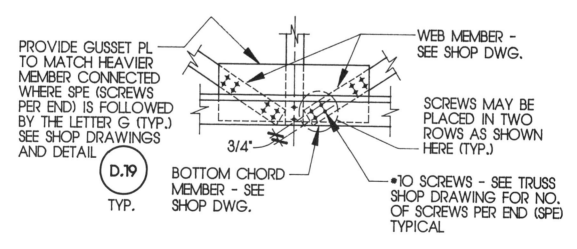

PROVIDE GUSSET PL TO MATCH HEAVIER MEMBER CONNECTED WHERE SPE (SCREWS PER END) IS FOLLOWED BY THE LETTER G (TYP.) SEE SHOP DRAWINGS AND DETAIL ( D.19 ) TYP.

WEB MEMBER - SEE SHOP DWG.

SCREWS MAY BE PLACED IN TWO ROWS AS SHOWN HERE (TYP.)

3/4"

BOTTOM CHORD MEMBER - SEE SHOP DWG.

#10 SCREWS - SEE TRUSS SHOP DRAWING FOR NO. OF SCREWS PER END (SPE) TYPICAL

## DETAIL AT BOTTOM CHORD

---

KING POST DETAIL

**D.4a**

# D. GUS TRUSS™ ROOF SYSTEM

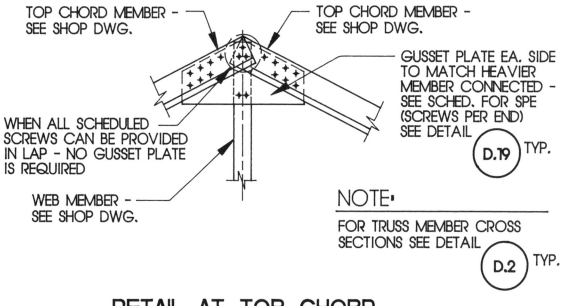

TOP CHORD MEMBER -
SEE SHOP DWG.

TOP CHORD MEMBER -
SEE SHOP DWG.

GUSSET PLATE EA. SIDE
TO MATCH HEAVIER
MEMBER CONNECTED -
SEE SCHED. FOR SPE
(SCREWS PER END)
SEE DETAIL

( D.19 ) TYP.

WHEN ALL SCHEDULED
SCREWS CAN BE PROVIDED
IN LAP - NO GUSSET PLATE
IS REQUIRED

WEB MEMBER -
SEE SHOP DWG.

NOTE:
FOR TRUSS MEMBER CROSS
SECTIONS SEE DETAIL

( D.2 ) TYP.

## DETAIL AT TOP CHORD

**NOTE:  GUSSET PLATE MAY NOT BE REQUIRED IF CALCULATED
NUMBER OF SCREWS CAN BE DIRECTLY APPLIED TO
ALL JOINED WEBS THROUGH CHORD MEMBER.**

**D.4b**        KING POST WITH GUSSET DETAIL

# D. GUS TRUSS™ ROOF SYSTEM

NOTE:

FOR TRUSS MEMBER CROSS
SECTIONS SEE DETAIL  D.2

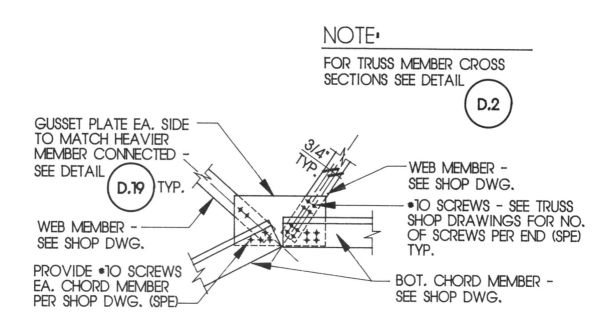

GUSSET PLATE EA. SIDE
TO MATCH HEAVIER
MEMBER CONNECTED -
SEE DETAIL D.19 TYP.

WEB MEMBER -
SEE SHOP DWG.

PROVIDE #10 SCREWS
EA. CHORD MEMBER
PER SHOP DWG. (SPE)

3/4" TYP.

WEB MEMBER -
SEE SHOP DWG.

#10 SCREWS - SEE TRUSS
SHOP DRAWINGS FOR NO.
OF SCREWS PER END (SPE)
TYP.

BOT. CHORD MEMBER -
SEE SHOP DWG.

## DETAIL AT BOTTOM CHORD

NOTE:  GUSSET PLATE MAY NOT BE REQUIRED IF CALCULATED
NUMBER OF SCREWS CAN BE DIRECTLY APPLIED TO
ALL JOINED WEBS THROGH CHORD MEMBER.

---

SCISSORS TRUSS WITH CLIPPED CEILING DETAIL     **D.5**

# D. GUS TRUSS™ ROOF SYSTEM

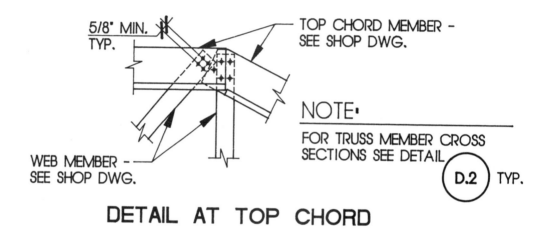

5/8" MIN. TYP.

TOP CHORD MEMBER –
SEE SHOP DWG.

NOTE:

FOR TRUSS MEMBER CROSS
SECTIONS SEE DETAIL

( D.2 ) TYP.

WEB MEMBER –
SEE SHOP DWG.

## DETAIL AT TOP CHORD

**NOTE:** GUSSET PLATE MAY NOT BE REQUIRED IF CALCULATED
NUMBER OF SCREWS CAN BE DIRECTLY APPLIED TO
ALL JOINED WEBS THROUGH CHORD MEMBER.

# D. GUS TRUSS™ ROOF SYSTEM

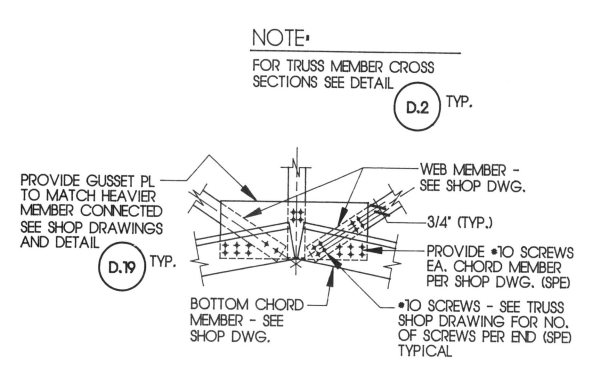

NOTE:

FOR TRUSS MEMBER CROSS
SECTIONS SEE DETAIL

( D.2 ) TYP.

PROVIDE GUSSET PL
TO MATCH HEAVIER
MEMBER CONNECTED
SEE SHOP DRAWINGS
AND DETAIL

( D.19 ) TYP.

WEB MEMBER -
SEE SHOP DWG.

3/4" (TYP.)

PROVIDE #10 SCREWS
EA. CHORD MEMBER
PER SHOP DWG. (SPE)

#10 SCREWS - SEE TRUSS
SHOP DRAWING FOR NO.
OF SCREWS PER END (SPE)
TYPICAL

BOTTOM CHORD
MEMBER - SEE
SHOP DWG.

## DETAIL AT BOTTOM CHORD

NOTE:  GUSSET PLATE MAY NOT BE REQUIRED IF CALCULATED
NUMBER OF SCREWS CAN BE DIRECTLY APPLIED TO
ALL JOINED WEBS THROUGH CHORD MEMBER.

---

SCISSORS TRUSS BOTTOM CHORD DETAIL          **D.7**

# D. GUS TRUSS™ ROOF SYSTEM

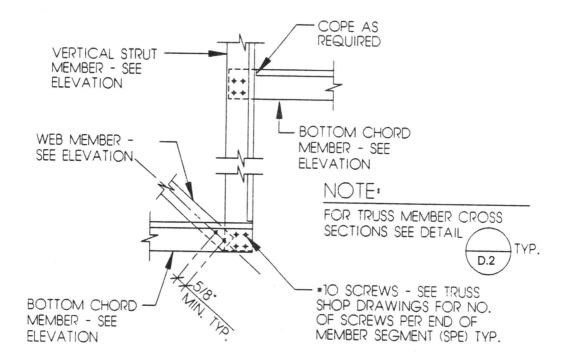

VERTICAL STRUT MEMBER - SEE ELEVATION

COPE AS REQUIRED

WEB MEMBER - SEE ELEVATION

BOTTOM CHORD MEMBER - SEE ELEVATION

NOTE:

FOR TRUSS MEMBER CROSS SECTIONS SEE DETAIL

D.2 TYP.

5/8" MIN. TYP.

BOTTOM CHORD MEMBER - SEE ELEVATION

*10 SCREWS - SEE TRUSS SHOP DRAWINGS FOR NO. OF SCREWS PER END OF MEMBER SEGMENT (SPE) TYP.

**COMPOSITE TRUSS DETAIL
(SCISSORS / COMMON)**

# D. GUS TRUSS™ ROOF SYSTEM

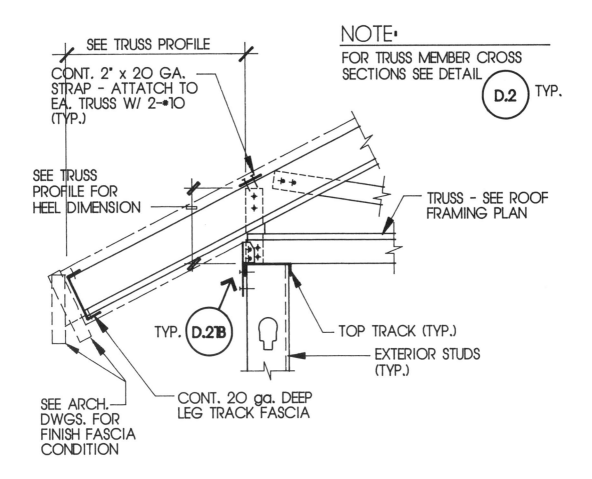

SEE TRUSS PROFILE

CONT. 2" x 20 GA.
STRAP - ATTATCH TO
EA. TRUSS W/ 2-#10
(TYP.)

SEE TRUSS
PROFILE FOR
HEEL DIMENSION

NOTE:
FOR TRUSS MEMBER CROSS
SECTIONS SEE DETAIL ( D.2 ) TYP.

TRUSS - SEE ROOF
FRAMING PLAN

TYP. ( D.2B )

TOP TRACK (TYP.)

EXTERIOR STUDS
(TYP.)

SEE ARCH.
DWGS. FOR
FINISH FASCIA
CONDITION

CONT. 20 ga. DEEP
LEG TRACK FASCIA

## OVERHANG DETAIL – FLAT BOTTOM CHORD          D.9

# D. GUS TRUSS™ ROOF SYSTEM

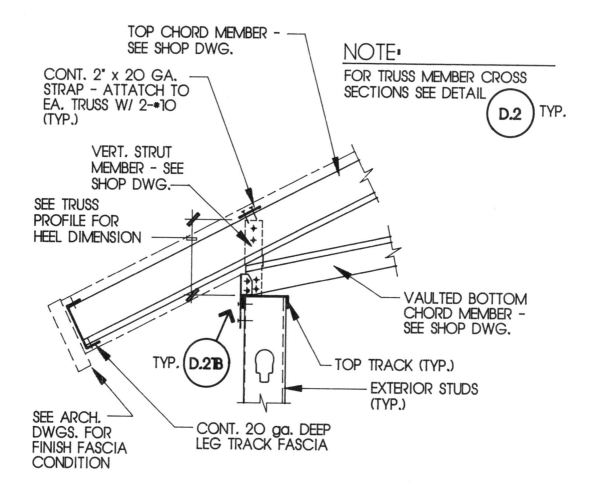

TOP CHORD MEMBER -
SEE SHOP DWG.

CONT. 2" x 20 GA.
STRAP - ATTATCH TO
EA. TRUSS W/ 2-#10
(TYP.)

VERT. STRUT
MEMBER - SEE
SHOP DWG.

SEE TRUSS
PROFILE FOR
HEEL DIMENSION

NOTE:
FOR TRUSS MEMBER CROSS
SECTIONS SEE DETAIL D.2 TYP.

VAULTED BOTTOM
CHORD MEMBER -
SEE SHOP DWG.

TYP. D.2B

TOP TRACK (TYP.)

EXTERIOR STUDS
(TYP.)

SEE ARCH.
DWGS. FOR
FINISH FASCIA
CONDITION

CONT. 20 ga. DEEP
LEG TRACK FASCIA

# D. GUS TRUSS™ ROOF SYSTEM

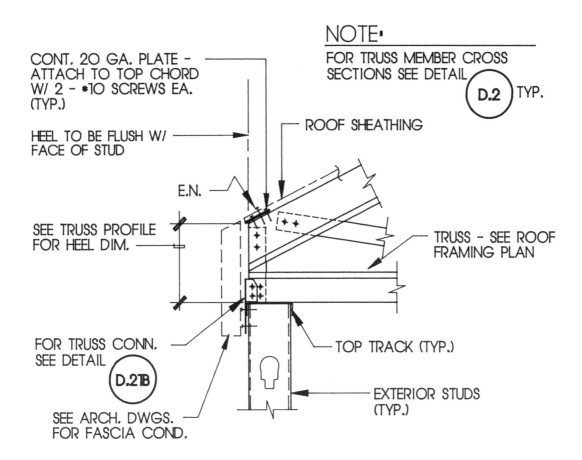

CONT. 20 GA. PLATE –
ATTACH TO TOP CHORD
W/ 2 - #10 SCREWS EA.
(TYP.)

HEEL TO BE FLUSH W/
FACE OF STUD

E.N.

SEE TRUSS PROFILE
FOR HEEL DIM.

FOR TRUSS CONN.
SEE DETAIL
( D.21B )

SEE ARCH. DWGS.
FOR FASCIA COND.

NOTE:
FOR TRUSS MEMBER CROSS
SECTIONS SEE DETAIL
( D.2 ) TYP.

ROOF SHEATHING

TRUSS - SEE ROOF
FRAMING PLAN

TOP TRACK (TYP.)

EXTERIOR STUDS
(TYP.)

# D. GUS TRUSS™ ROOF SYSTEM

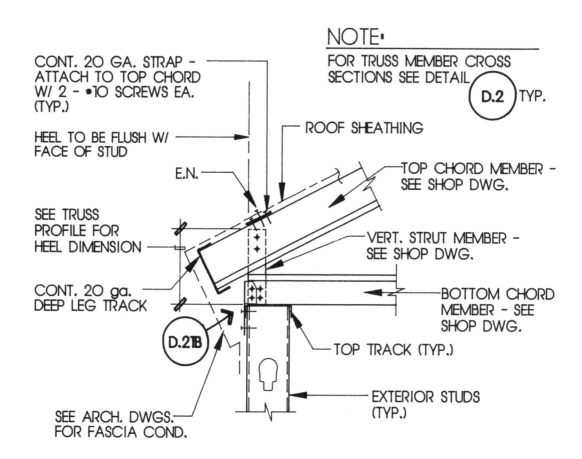

CONT. 20 GA. STRAP –
ATTACH TO TOP CHORD
W/ 2 - #10 SCREWS EA.
(TYP.)

HEEL TO BE FLUSH W/
FACE OF STUD

SEE TRUSS
PROFILE FOR
HEEL DIMENSION

CONT. 20 ga.
DEEP LEG TRACK

SEE ARCH. DWGS.
FOR FASCIA COND.

E.N.

NOTE:
FOR TRUSS MEMBER CROSS
SECTIONS SEE DETAIL ( D.2 ) TYP.

ROOF SHEATHING

TOP CHORD MEMBER –
SEE SHOP DWG.

VERT. STRUT MEMBER –
SEE SHOP DWG.

BOTTOM CHORD
MEMBER - SEE
SHOP DWG.

TOP TRACK (TYP.)

EXTERIOR STUDS
(TYP.)

D.21B

**D.12**     ZERO OVERHANG DETAIL – RAKED FASCIA

# D. GUS TRUSS™ ROOF SYSTEM

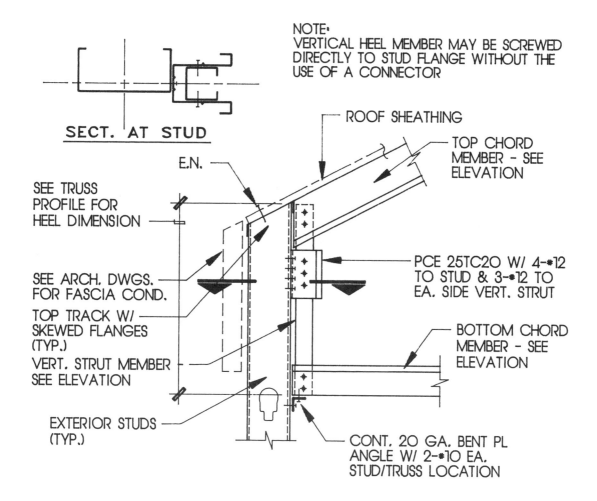

**SECT. AT STUD**

NOTE·
VERTICAL HEEL MEMBER MAY BE SCREWED
DIRECTLY TO STUD FLANGE WITHOUT THE
USE OF A CONNECTOR

ROOF SHEATHING

TOP CHORD
MEMBER - SEE
ELEVATION

E.N.

SEE TRUSS
PROFILE FOR
HEEL DIMENSION

PCE 25TC20 W/ 4-#12
TO STUD & 3-#12 TO
EA. SIDE VERT. STRUT

SEE ARCH. DWGS.
FOR FASCIA COND.

BOTTOM CHORD
MEMBER - SEE
ELEVATION

TOP TRACK W/
SKEWED FLANGES
(TYP.)

VERT. STRUT MEMBER
SEE ELEVATION

EXTERIOR STUDS
(TYP.)

CONT. 20 GA. BENT PL
ANGLE W/ 2-#10 EA.
STUD/TRUSS LOCATION

---

TRUSS CONNECTION TO FACE OF STUD **D.13a**

# D. GUS TRUSS™ ROOF SYSTEM

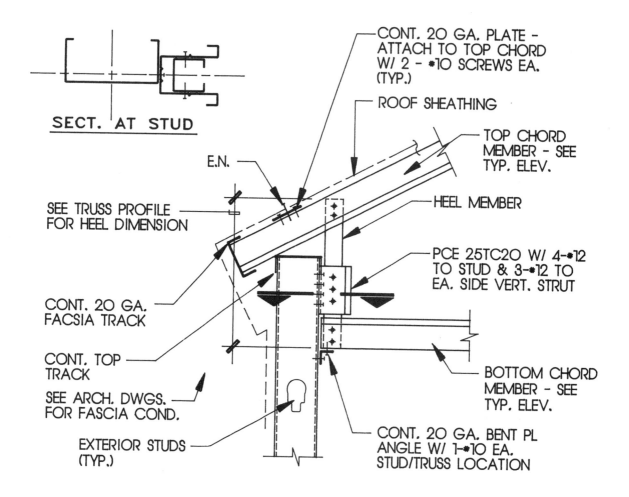

SECT. AT STUD

CONT. 20 GA. PLATE –
ATTACH TO TOP CHORD
W/ 2 - #10 SCREWS EA.
(TYP.)

ROOF SHEATHING

TOP CHORD
MEMBER - SEE
TYP. ELEV.

HEEL MEMBER

PCE 25TC20 W/ 4-#12
TO STUD & 3-#12 TO
EA. SIDE VERT. STRUT

BOTTOM CHORD
MEMBER - SEE
TYP. ELEV.

CONT. 20 GA. BENT PL
ANGLE W/ 1-#10 EA.
STUD/TRUSS LOCATION

E.N.

SEE TRUSS PROFILE
FOR HEEL DIMENSION

CONT. 20 GA.
FACSIA TRACK

CONT. TOP
TRACK

SEE ARCH. DWGS.
FOR FASCIA COND.

EXTERIOR STUDS
(TYP.)

**D.13b**     TRUSS CONNECTION TO FACE OF STUD

# D. GUS TRUSS™ ROOF SYSTEM

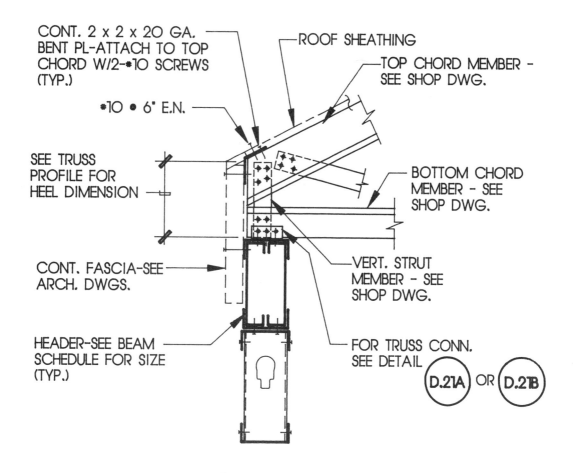

CONT. 2 x 2 x 20 GA.
BENT PL-ATTACH TO TOP
CHORD W/2-#10 SCREWS
(TYP.)

#10 @ 6" E.N.

SEE TRUSS
PROFILE FOR
HEEL DIMENSION

CONT. FASCIA-SEE
ARCH. DWGS.

HEADER-SEE BEAM
SCHEDULE FOR SIZE
(TYP.)

ROOF SHEATHING

TOP CHORD MEMBER -
SEE SHOP DWG.

BOTTOM CHORD
MEMBER - SEE
SHOP DWG.

VERT. STRUT
MEMBER - SEE
SHOP DWG.

FOR TRUSS CONN.
SEE DETAIL

D.21A OR D.21B

## TRUSS CONNECTION TO HEADER – ZERO OVERHANG

**D.14**

# D. GUS TRUSS™ ROOF SYSTEM

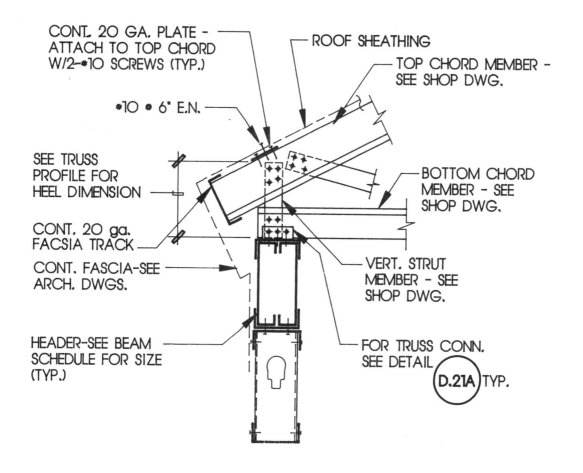

CONT. 20 GA. PLATE - ATTACH TO TOP CHORD W/2-#10 SCREWS (TYP.)

ROOF SHEATHING

TOP CHORD MEMBER - SEE SHOP DWG.

#10 @ 6" E.N.

SEE TRUSS PROFILE FOR HEEL DIMENSION

BOTTOM CHORD MEMBER - SEE SHOP DWG.

CONT. 20 ga. FACSIA TRACK

CONT. FASCIA-SEE ARCH. DWGS.

VERT. STRUT MEMBER - SEE SHOP DWG.

HEADER-SEE BEAM SCHEDULE FOR SIZE (TYP.)

FOR TRUSS CONN. SEE DETAIL D.21A TYP.

**D.15**   TRUSS CONNECTION TO HEADER – RAKED FASCIA

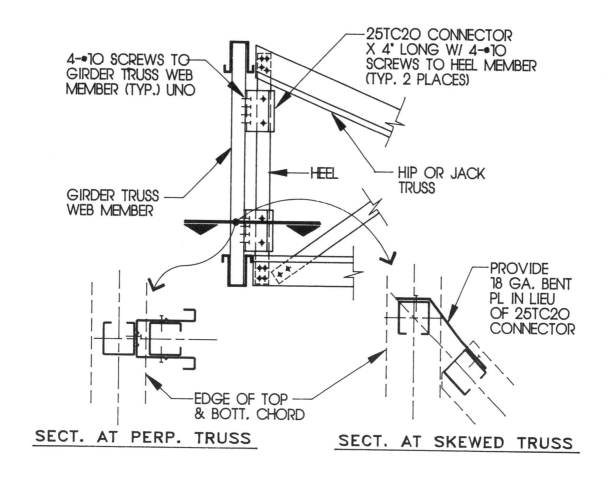

4-#10 SCREWS TO
GIRDER TRUSS WEB
MEMBER (TYP.) UNO

25TC20 CONNECTOR
X 4" LONG W/ 4-#10
SCREWS TO HEEL MEMBER
(TYP. 2 PLACES)

HEEL

HIP OR JACK
TRUSS

GIRDER TRUSS
WEB MEMBER

PROVIDE
18 GA. BENT
PL IN LIEU
OF 25TC20
CONNECTOR

EDGE OF TOP
& BOTT. CHORD

SECT. AT PERP. TRUSS

SECT. AT SKEWED TRUSS

# D. GUS TRUSS™ ROOF SYSTEM

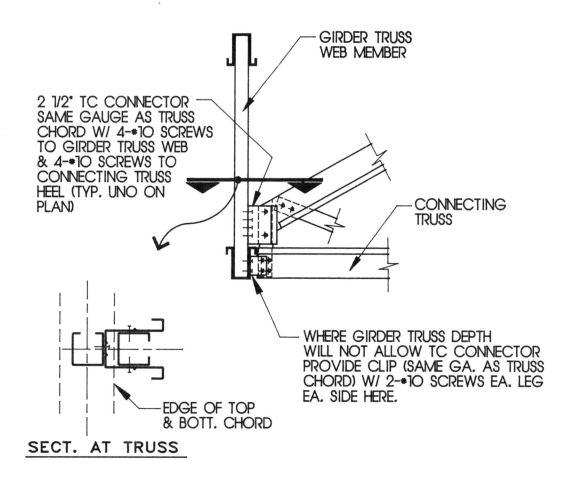

GIRDER TRUSS
WEB MEMBER

2 1/2" TC CONNECTOR
SAME GAUGE AS TRUSS
CHORD W/ 4-#10 SCREWS
TO GIRDER TRUSS WEB
& 4-#10 SCREWS TO
CONNECTING TRUSS
HEEL (TYP. UNO ON
PLAN)

CONNECTING
TRUSS

WHERE GIRDER TRUSS DEPTH
WILL NOT ALLOW TC CONNECTOR
PROVIDE CLIP (SAME GA. AS TRUSS
CHORD) W/ 2-#10 SCREWS EA. LEG
EA. SIDE HERE.

EDGE OF TOP
& BOTT. CHORD

**SECT. AT TRUSS**

# D. GUS TRUSS™ ROOF SYSTEM

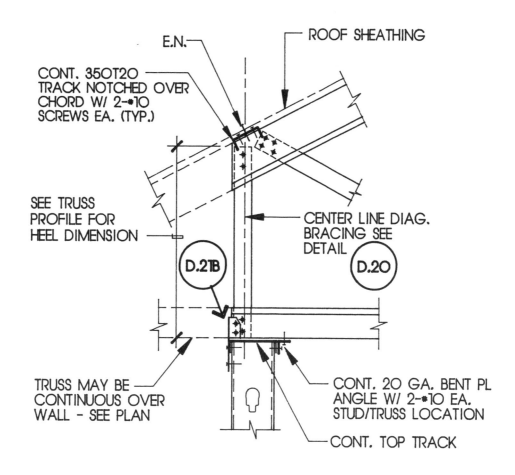

E.N.

ROOF SHEATHING

CONT. 35OT2O
TRACK NOTCHED OVER
CHORD W/ 2-#10
SCREWS EA. (TYP.)

SEE TRUSS
PROFILE FOR
HEEL DIMENSION

CENTER LINE DIAG.
BRACING SEE
DETAIL

D.21B

D.20

TRUSS MAY BE
CONTINUOUS OVER
WALL – SEE PLAN

CONT. 20 GA. BENT PL
ANGLE W/ 2-#10 EA.
STUD/TRUSS LOCATION

CONT. TOP TRACK

---

## BLOCKED TRUSS HEEL SECTION  D.18

# D. GUS TRUSS™ ROOF SYSTEM

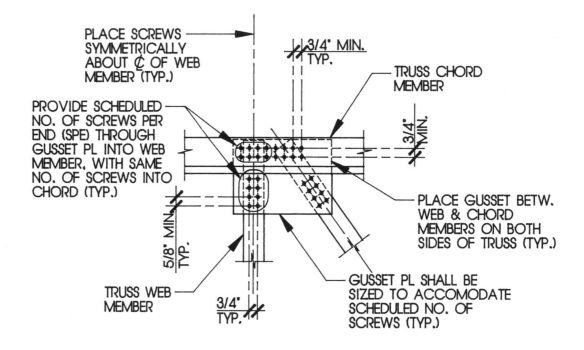

PLACE SCREWS SYMMETRICALLY ABOUT ℄ OF WEB MEMBER (TYP.)

3/4" MIN. TYP.

TRUSS CHORD MEMBER

PROVIDE SCHEDULED NO. OF SCREWS PER END (SPE) THROUGH GUSSET PL INTO WEB MEMBER, WITH SAME NO. OF SCREWS INTO CHORD (TYP.)

3/4" MIN.

PLACE GUSSET BETW. WEB & CHORD MEMBERS ON BOTH SIDES OF TRUSS (TYP.)

5/8" MIN. TYP.

TRUSS WEB MEMBER

3/4" TYP.

GUSSET PL SHALL BE SIZED TO ACCOMODATE SCHEDULED NO. OF SCREWS (TYP.)

# D. GUS TRUSS™ ROOF SYSTEM

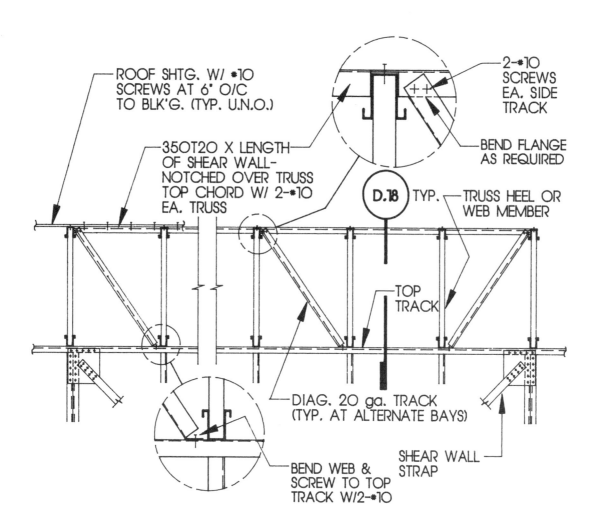

ROOF SHTG. W/ *10 SCREWS AT 6" O/C TO BLK'G. (TYP. U.N.O.)

350T20 X LENGTH OF SHEAR WALL- NOTCHED OVER TRUSS TOP CHORD W/ 2-*10 EA. TRUSS

2-*10 SCREWS EA. SIDE TRACK

BEND FLANGE AS REQUIRED

D.18 TYP.

TRUSS HEEL OR WEB MEMBER

TOP TRACK

DIAG. 20 ga. TRACK (TYP. AT ALTERNATE BAYS)

BEND WEB & SCREW TO TOP TRACK W/2-*10

SHEAR WALL STRAP

---

## TRUSS BLOCKING DETAIL                    D.20

# D. GUS TRUSS™ ROOF SYSTEM

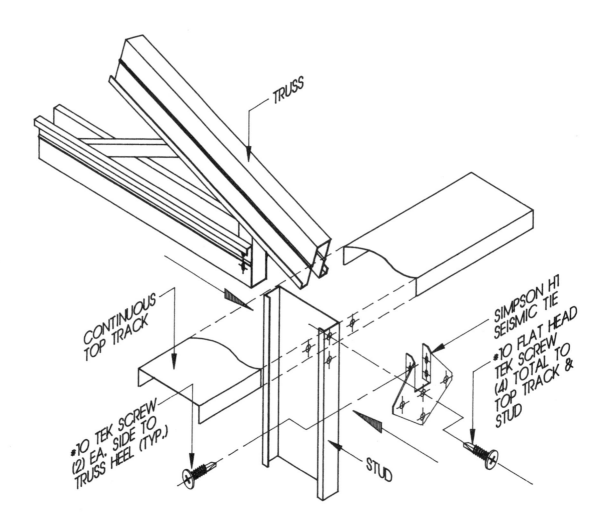

TRUSS

CONTINUOUS TOP TRACK

SIMPSON H1 SEISMIC TIE

#10 FLAT HEAD TEK SCREW (4) TOTAL TO TOP TRACK & STUD

#10 TEK SCREW (2) EA. SIDE TO TRUSS HEEL (TYP.)

STUD

**D.21**  GUSS TRUSS™ TO TOP TRACK DETAIL

# D. GUS TRUSS™ ROOF SYSTEM

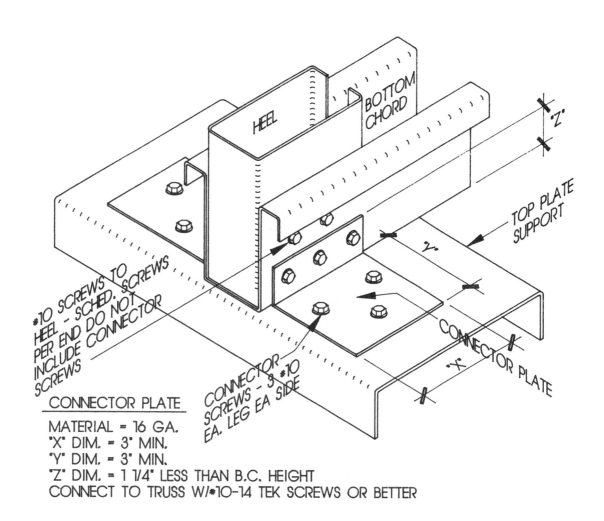

**HEEL**

**BOTTOM CHORD**

'Z'

TOP PLATE SUPPORT

#10 SCREWS TO HEEL - SCHED. SCREWS PER END DO NOT INCLUDE CONNECTOR SCREWS

'Y'

CONNECTOR PLATE

'X'

CONNECTOR SCREWS - 3 #10 EA. LEG EA SIDE

CONNECTOR PLATE

MATERIAL = 16 GA.
"X" DIM. = 3" MIN.
"Y" DIM. = 3" MIN.
"Z" DIM. = 1 1/4" LESS THAN B.C. HEIGHT
CONNECT TO TRUSS W/#10-14 TEK SCREWS OR BETTER

---

## BOTTOM CHORD TO TOP PLATE
## CONNECTION DETAIL

**D.21a**

# D. GUS TRUSS™ ROOF SYSTEM

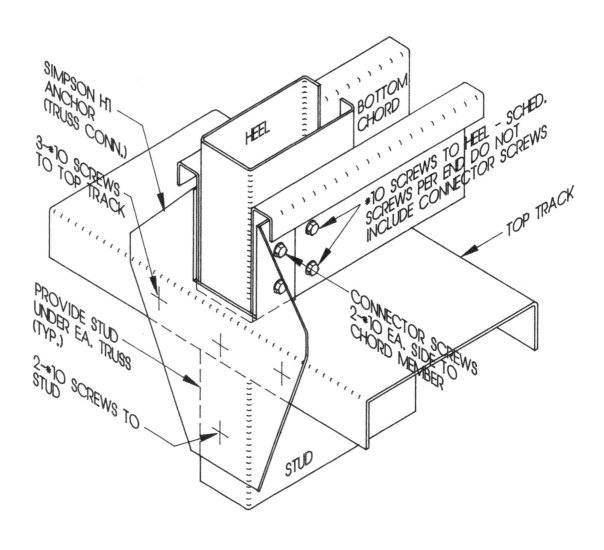

SIMPSON H1
ANCHOR
(TRUSS CONN.)

3-#10 SCREWS
TO TOP TRACK

HEEL

BOTTOM
CHORD

#10 SCREWS TO HEEL - SCHED.
SCREWS PER END DO NOT
INCLUDE CONNECTOR SCREWS

TOP TRACK

PROVIDE STUD
UNDER EA. TRUSS
(TYP.)

2-#10 SCREWS TO
STUD

CONNECTOR SCREWS
2-#10 EA. SIDE TO
CHORD MEMBER

STUD

---

**D.21b**          BOTTOM CHORD TO TOP PLATE
                   CONNECTION DETAIL

# D. GUS TRUSS™ ROOF SYSTEM

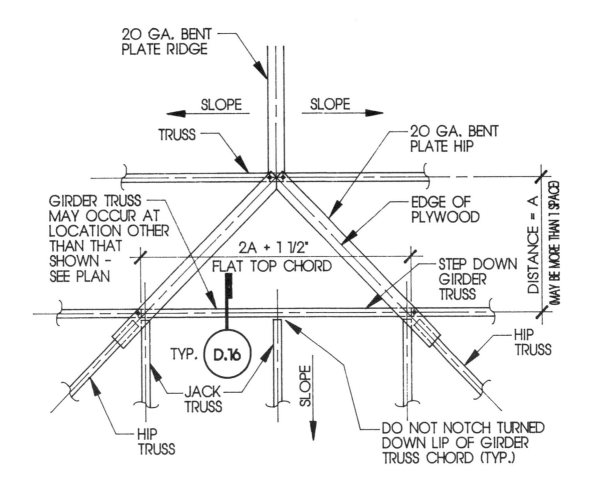

20 GA. BENT PLATE RIDGE

SLOPE ← → SLOPE

TRUSS

20 GA. BENT PLATE HIP

GIRDER TRUSS MAY OCCUR AT LOCATION OTHER THAN THAT SHOWN - SEE PLAN

EDGE OF PLYWOOD

2A + 1 1/2" FLAT TOP CHORD

STEP DOWN GIRDER TRUSS

DISTANCE = A (MAY BE MORE THAN 1 SPACE)

TYP. D.16

JACK TRUSS

SLOPE

HIP TRUSS

HIP TRUSS

DO NOT NOTCH TURNED DOWN LIP OF GIRDER TRUSS CHORD (TYP.)

---

TYPICAL HIP ROOF PLAN                    **D.22**

# D. GUS TRUSS™ ROOF SYSTEM

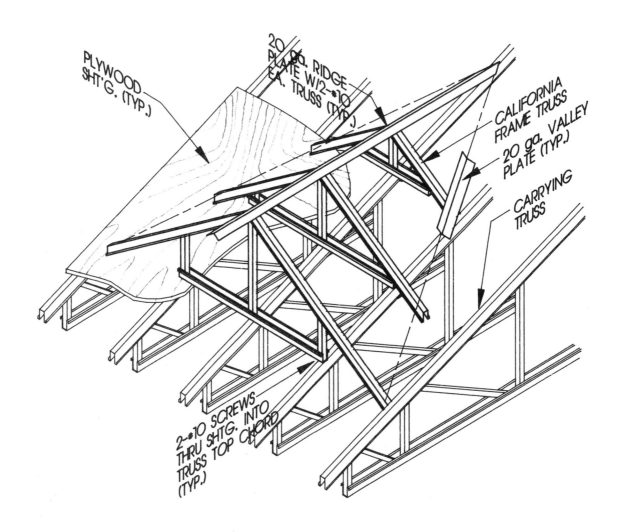

PLYWOOD SHT'G. (TYP.)

20 ga. RIDGE PLATE W/2-#10 EA. TRUSS (TYP.)

CALIFORNIA FRAME TRUSS

20 ga. VALLEY PLATE (TYP.)

CARRYING TRUSS

2-#10 SCREWS THRU SHTG. INTO TRUSS TOP CHORD (TYP.)

---

**D.23**

TYPICAL OVERFRAME
(CALIFORNIA FRAMING) TRUSSES

# D. GUS TRUSS™ ROOF SYSTEM

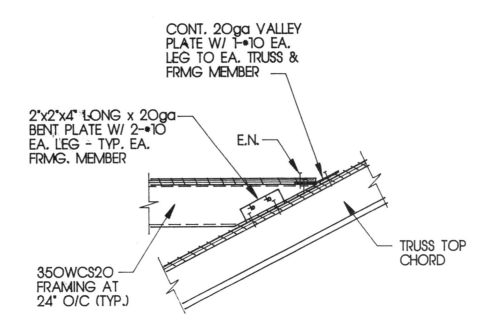

CONT. 20ga VALLEY
PLATE W/ 1-#10 EA.
LEG TO EA. TRUSS &
FRMG MEMBER

2"x2"x4" LONG x 20ga
BENT PLATE W/ 2-#10
EA. LEG - TYP. EA.
FRMG. MEMBER

E.N.

TRUSS TOP
CHORD

350WCS20
FRAMING AT
24" O/C (TYP.)

---

TYPICAL OVERFRAME DETAIL **D.23a**

# D. GUS TRUSS™ ROOF SYSTEM

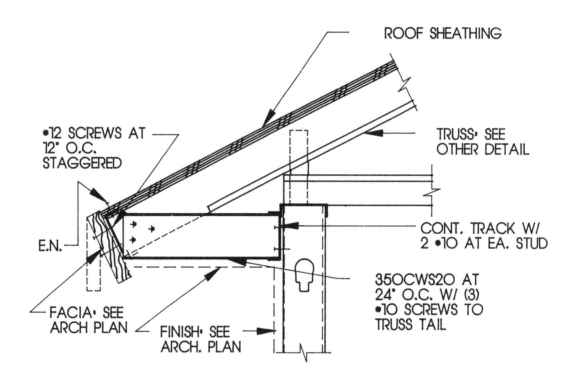

ROOF SHEATHING

#12 SCREWS AT
12" O.C.
STAGGERED

TRUSS· SEE
OTHER DETAIL

E.N.

CONT. TRACK W/
2 #10 AT EA. STUD

FACIA· SEE
ARCH PLAN

FINISH· SEE
ARCH. PLAN

350CWS20 AT
24" O.C. W/ (3)
#10 SCREWS TO
TRUSS TAIL

**D.24**     TYPICAL SOFFIT FRAMING DETAIL

# D. GUS TRUSS™ ROOF SYSTEM

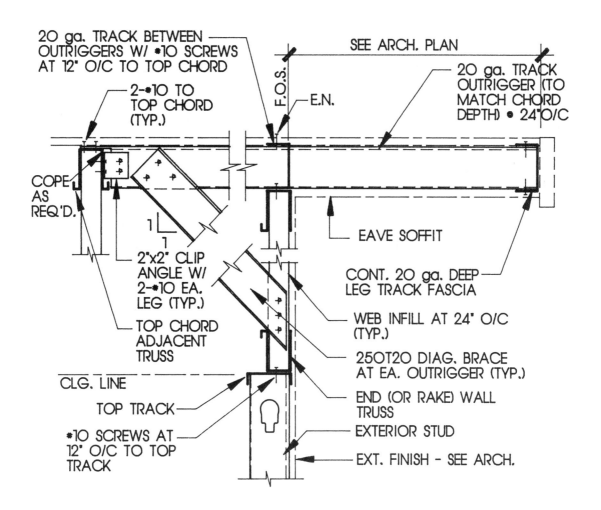

20 ga. TRACK BETWEEN OUTRIGGERS W/ #10 SCREWS AT 12" O/C TO TOP CHORD

2-#10 TO TOP CHORD (TYP.)

SEE ARCH. PLAN

F.O.S.

E.N.

20 ga. TRACK OUTRIGGER (TO MATCH CHORD DEPTH) ● 24" O/C

COPE AS REQ'D.

2"x2" CLIP ANGLE W/ 2-#10 EA. LEG (TYP.)

TOP CHORD ADJACENT TRUSS

EAVE SOFFIT

CONT. 20 ga. DEEP LEG TRACK FASCIA

WEB INFILL AT 24" O/C (TYP.)

250T20 DIAG. BRACE AT EA. OUTRIGGER (TYP.)

END (OR RAKE) WALL TRUSS

EXTERIOR STUD

EXT. FINISH - SEE ARCH.

CLG. LINE

TOP TRACK

#10 SCREWS AT 12" O/C TO TOP TRACK

---

## SECTION AT RAKE WALL TRUSS

**D.25**

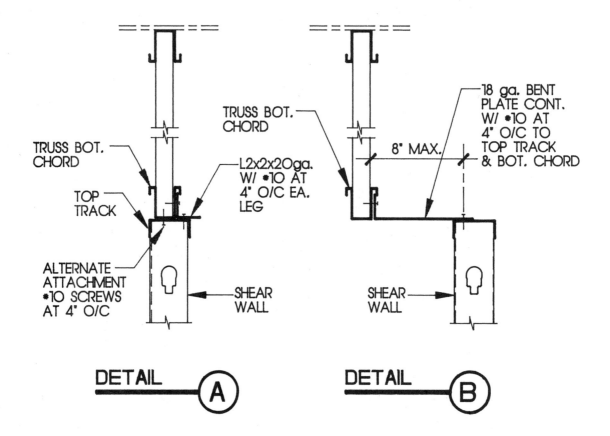

TRUSS BOT. CHORD

TRUSS BOT. CHORD

TOP TRACK

L2x2x20ga. W/ #10 AT 4" O/C EA. LEG

ALTERNATE ATTACHMENT #10 SCREWS AT 4" O/C

SHEAR WALL

**DETAIL** (A)

TRUSS BOT. CHORD

8" MAX.

18 ga. BENT PLATE CONT. W/ #10 AT 4" O/C TO TOP TRACK & BOT. CHORD

SHEAR WALL

**DETAIL** (B)

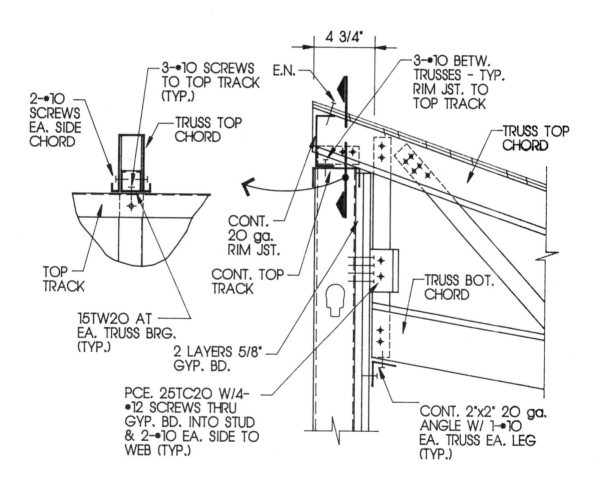

2-#10
SCREWS
EA. SIDE
CHORD

3-#10 SCREWS
TO TOP TRACK
(TYP.)

TRUSS TOP
CHORD

4 3/4"

E.N.

3-#10 BETW.
TRUSSES - TYP.
RIM JST. TO
TOP TRACK

TRUSS TOP
CHORD

TOP
TRACK

15TW20 AT
EA. TRUSS BRG.
(TYP.)

2 LAYERS 5/8"
GYP. BD.

CONT.
20 ga.
RIM JST.

CONT. TOP
TRACK

TRUSS BOT.
CHORD

PCE. 25TC20 W/4-
#12 SCREWS THRU
GYP. BD. INTO STUD
& 2-#10 EA. SIDE TO
WEB (TYP.)

CONT. 2"x2" 20 ga.
ANGLE W/ 1-#10
EA. TRUSS EA. LEG
(TYP.)

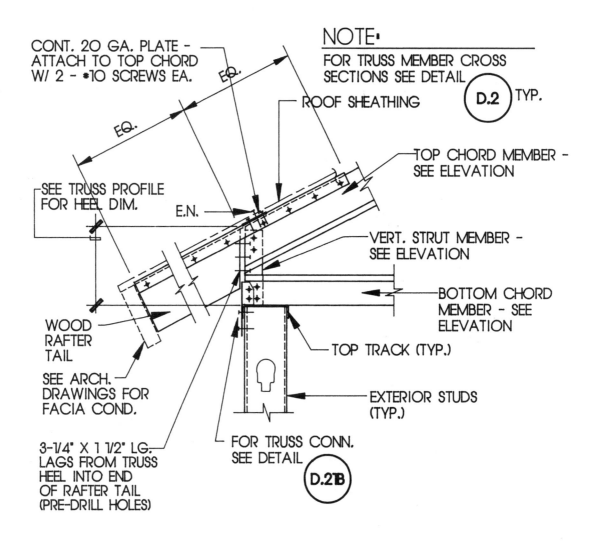

CONT. 20 GA. PLATE -
ATTACH TO TOP CHORD
W/ 2 - #10 SCREWS EA.

EQ.

EQ.

EQ.

SEE TRUSS PROFILE
FOR HEEL DIM.

E.N.

WOOD
RAFTER
TAIL

SEE ARCH.
DRAWINGS FOR
FACIA COND.

3-1/4" X 1 1/2" LG.
LAGS FROM TRUSS
HEEL INTO END
OF RAFTER TAIL
(PRE-DRILL HOLES)

NOTE:
FOR TRUSS MEMBER CROSS
SECTIONS SEE DETAIL  D.2  TYP.

ROOF SHEATHING

TOP CHORD MEMBER -
SEE ELEVATION

VERT. STRUT MEMBER -
SEE ELEVATION

BOTTOM CHORD
MEMBER - SEE
ELEVATION

TOP TRACK (TYP.)

EXTERIOR STUDS
(TYP.)

FOR TRUSS CONN.
SEE DETAIL  D.28

**D.28**      WOOD RAFTER TAIL CONNECTION
TO GUS TRUSS™

# D. GUS TRUSS™ ROOF SYSTEM

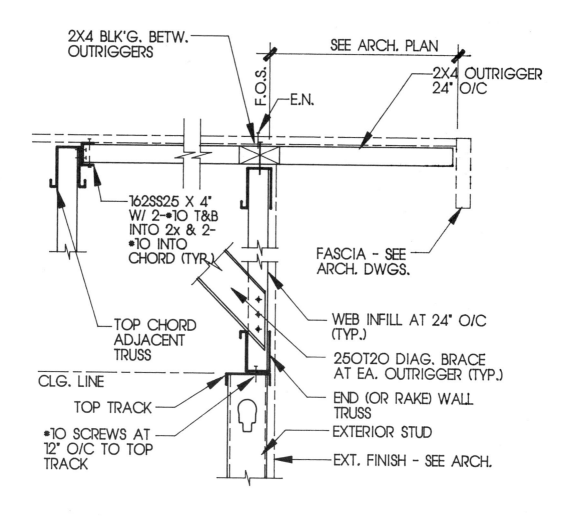

2X4 BLK'G. BETW. OUTRIGGERS

SEE ARCH. PLAN

F.O.S.

E.N.

2X4 OUTRIGGER 24" O/C

162SS25 X 4" W/ 2-#10 T&B INTO 2x & 2- #10 INTO CHORD (TYP.)

FASCIA - SEE ARCH. DWGS.

TOP CHORD ADJACENT TRUSS

WEB INFILL AT 24" O/C (TYP.)

CLG. LINE

250T20 DIAG. BRACE AT EA. OUTRIGGER (TYP.)

TOP TRACK

END (OR RAKE) WALL TRUSS

#10 SCREWS AT 12" O/C TO TOP TRACK

EXTERIOR STUD

EXT. FINISH - SEE ARCH.

## SECTION AT RAKE WALL TRUSS WITH WOOD OUTRIGGERS

**D.29**

# D. GUS TRUSS™ ROOF SYSTEM

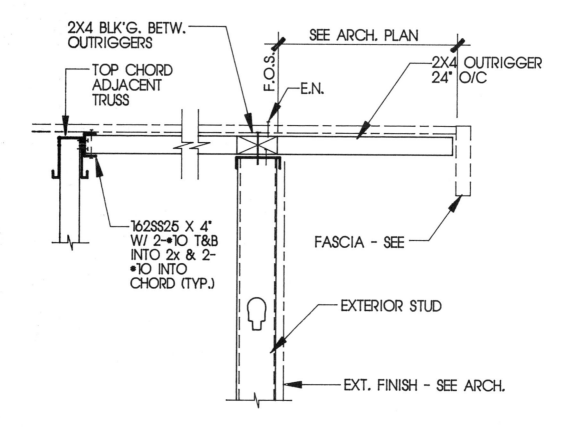

2X4 BLK'G. BETW. OUTRIGGERS

TOP CHORD ADJACENT TRUSS

SEE ARCH. PLAN

F.O.S.

E.N.

2X4 OUTRIGGER 24" O/C

162SS25 X 4" W/ 2-#10 T&B INTO 2x & 2-#10 INTO CHORD (TYP.)

FASCIA - SEE

EXTERIOR STUD

EXT. FINISH - SEE ARCH.

# D. GUS TRUSS™ ROOF SYSTEM

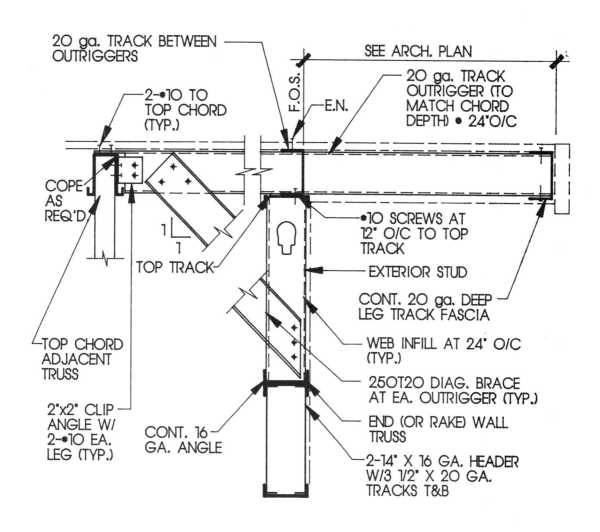

20 ga. TRACK BETWEEN OUTRIGGERS

2-#10 TO TOP CHORD (TYP.)

SEE ARCH. PLAN

F.O.S.

E.N.

20 ga. TRACK OUTRIGGER (TO MATCH CHORD DEPTH) • 24"O/C

COPE AS REQ'D.

1
1

TOP TRACK

#10 SCREWS AT 12" O/C TO TOP TRACK

EXTERIOR STUD

CONT. 20 ga. DEEP LEG TRACK FASCIA

WEB INFILL AT 24" O/C (TYP.)

TOP CHORD ADJACENT TRUSS

2"x2" CLIP ANGLE W/ 2-#10 EA. LEG (TYP.)

CONT. 16 GA. ANGLE

25OT2O DIAG. BRACE AT EA. OUTRIGGER (TYP.)

END (OR RAKE) WALL TRUSS

2-14" X 16 GA. HEADER W/3 1/2" X 20 GA. TRACKS T&B

## SECTION AT BALLOON FRAMED RAKE WALL OVER OPENING

**D.31**

# D. GUS TRUSS™ ROOF SYSTEM

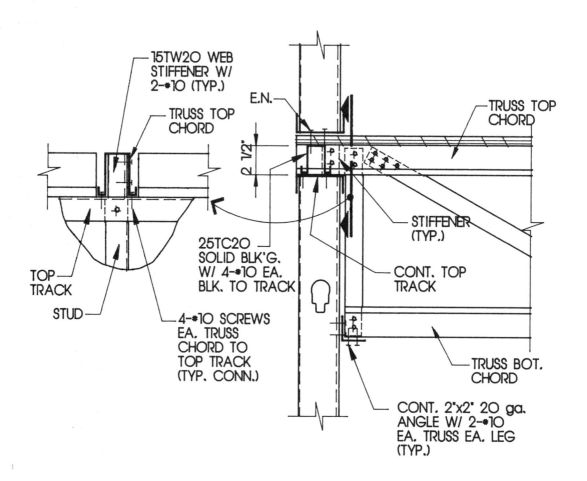

15TW20 WEB STIFFENER W/ 2-#10 (TYP.)

TRUSS TOP CHORD

E.N.

TRUSS TOP CHORD

2 1/2"

STIFFENER (TYP.)

TOP TRACK

STUD

25TC20 SOLID BLK'G. W/ 4-#10 EA. BLK. TO TRACK

CONT. TOP TRACK

4-#10 SCREWS EA. TRUSS CHORD TO TOP TRACK (TYP. CONN.)

TRUSS BOT. CHORD

CONT. 2"x2" 20 ga. ANGLE W/ 2-#10 EA. TRUSS EA. LEG (TYP.)

**D.32a**    TOP CHORD BEARING FLOOR TRUSS DETAIL

# D. GUS TRUSS™ ROOF SYSTEM

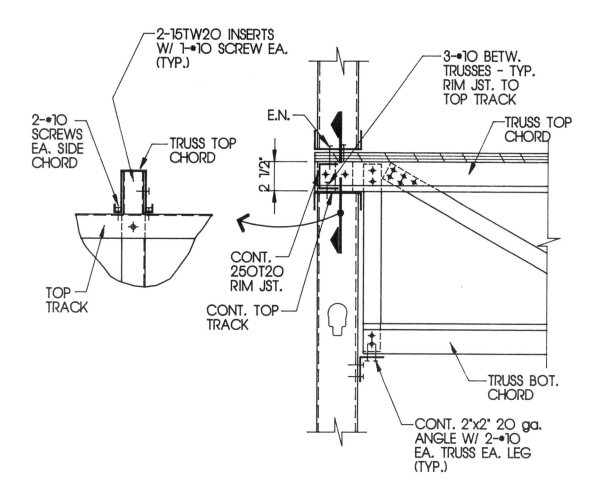

2-15TW20 INSERTS
W/ 1-#10 SCREW EA.
(TYP.)

2-#10
SCREWS
EA. SIDE
CHORD

TRUSS TOP
CHORD

TOP
TRACK

3-#10 BETW.
TRUSSES - TYP.
RIM JST. TO
TOP TRACK

E.N.

2 1/2"

TRUSS TOP
CHORD

CONT.
250T20
RIM JST.

CONT. TOP
TRACK

TRUSS BOT.
CHORD

CONT. 2"x2" 20 ga.
ANGLE W/ 2-#10
EA. TRUSS EA. LEG
(TYP.)

## TOP CHORD BEARING FLOOR TRUSS DETAIL
## (ALTERNATE)

**D.32b**

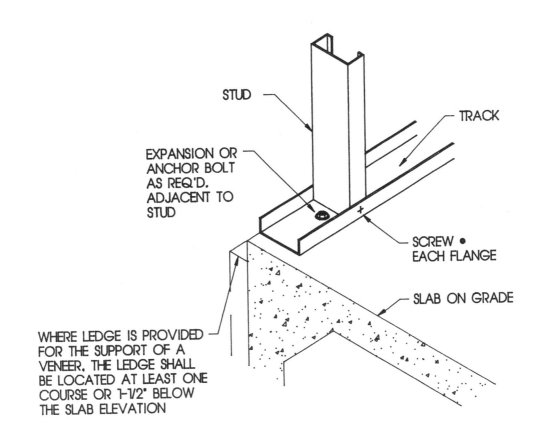

STUD

TRACK

EXPANSION OR
ANCHOR BOLT
AS REQ'D.
ADJACENT TO
STUD

SCREW •
EACH FLANGE

SLAB ON GRADE

WHERE LEDGE IS PROVIDED
FOR THE SUPPORT OF A
VENEER, THE LEDGE SHALL
BE LOCATED AT LEAST ONE
COURSE OR 1-1/2" BELOW
THE SLAB ELEVATION

## BASE OF WALL AT SLAB ON GRADE

**E.1**

# E. DETAILS AT EXTERIOR WALLS

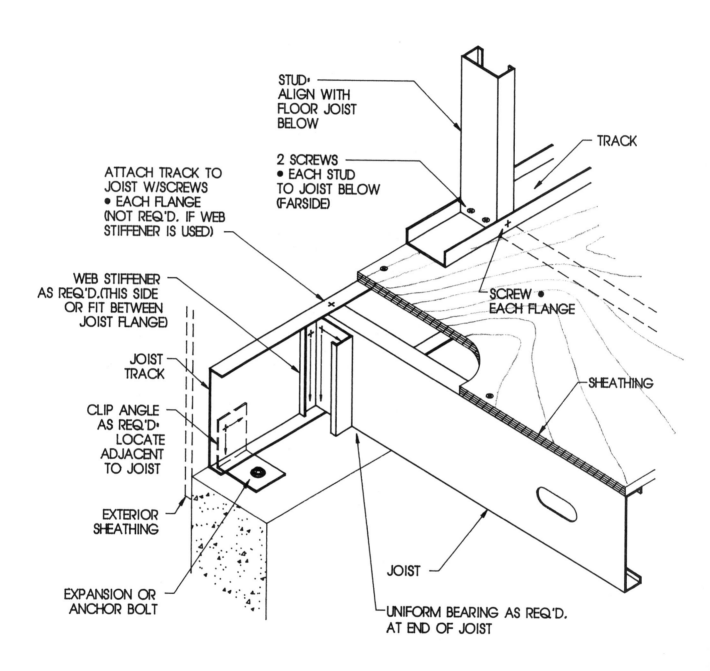

STUD·
ALIGN WITH
FLOOR JOIST
BELOW

TRACK

ATTACH TRACK TO
JOIST W/SCREWS
● EACH FLANGE
(NOT REQ'D. IF WEB
STIFFENER IS USED)

2 SCREWS
● EACH STUD
TO JOIST BELOW
(FARSIDE)

SCREW ●
EACH FLANGE

WEB STIFFENER
AS REQ'D.(THIS SIDE
OR FIT BETWEEN
JOIST FLANGE)

JOIST
TRACK

CLIP ANGLE
AS REQ'D·
LOCATE
ADJACENT
TO JOIST

SHEATHING

EXTERIOR
SHEATHING

EXPANSION OR
ANCHOR BOLT

JOIST

UNIFORM BEARING AS REQ'D.
AT END OF JOIST

---

**E.2**    FLOOR JOISTS BEARING ON FOUNDATION

# E. DETAILS AT EXTERIOR WALLS

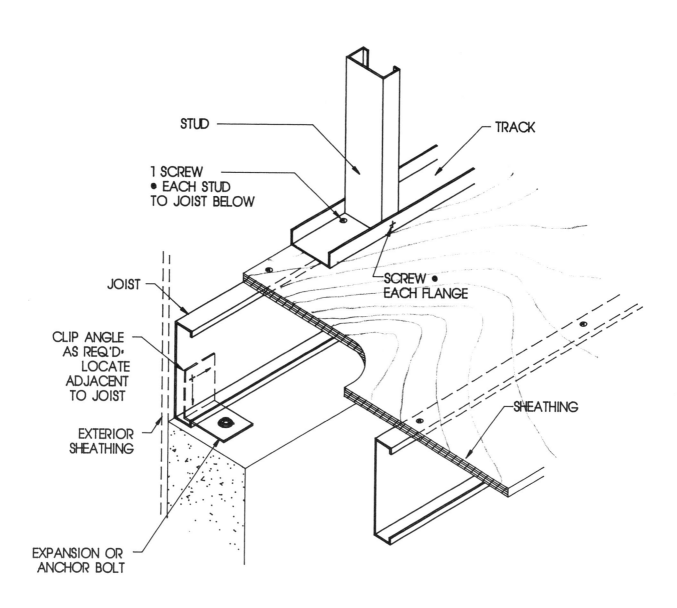

STUD

TRACK

1 SCREW
• EACH STUD
TO JOIST BELOW

SCREW •
EACH FLANGE

JOIST

CLIP ANGLE
AS REQ'D•
LOCATE
ADJACENT
TO JOIST

EXTERIOR
SHEATHING

SHEATHING

EXPANSION OR
ANCHOR BOLT

---

## FLOOR JOISTS PARALLEL TO FOUNDATION

**E.3**

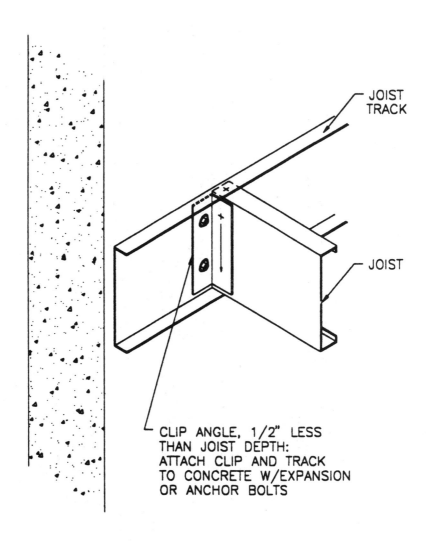

JOIST
TRACK

JOIST

CLIP ANGLE, 1/2" LESS
THAN JOIST DEPTH;
ATTACH CLIP AND TRACK
TO CONCRETE W/EXPANSION
OR ANCHOR BOLTS

# E. DETAILS AT EXTERIOR WALLS

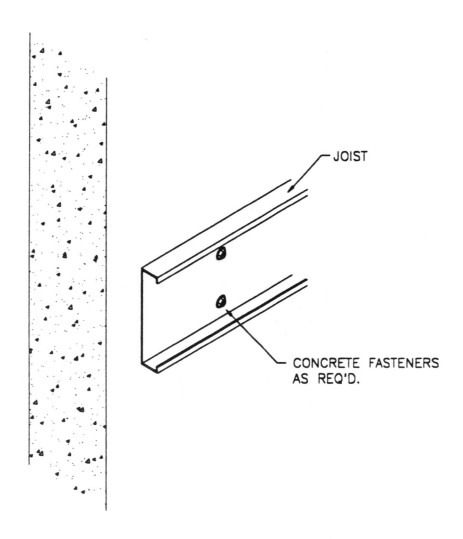

JOIST

CONCRETE FASTENERS
AS REQ'D.

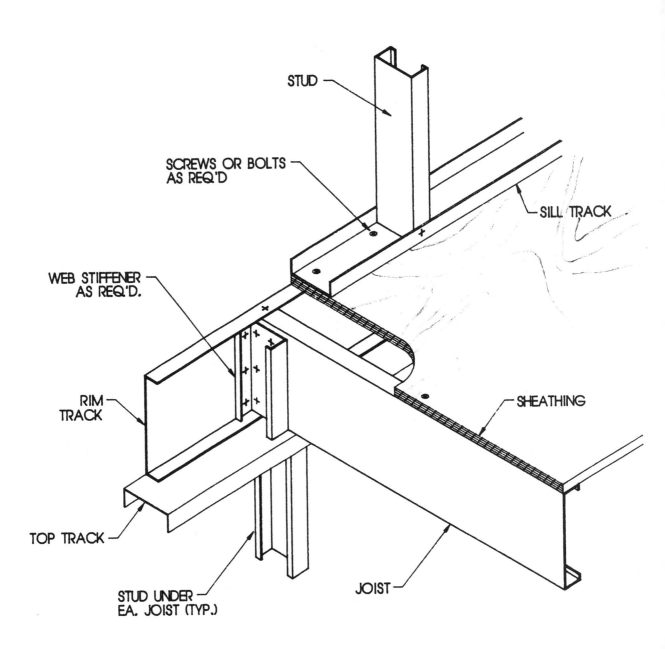

STUD

SCREWS OR BOLTS
AS REQ'D

SILL TRACK

WEB STIFFENER
AS REQ'D.

RIM
TRACK

SHEATHING

TOP TRACK

STUD UNDER
EA. JOIST (TYP.)

JOIST

# E. DETAILS AT EXTERIOR WALLS

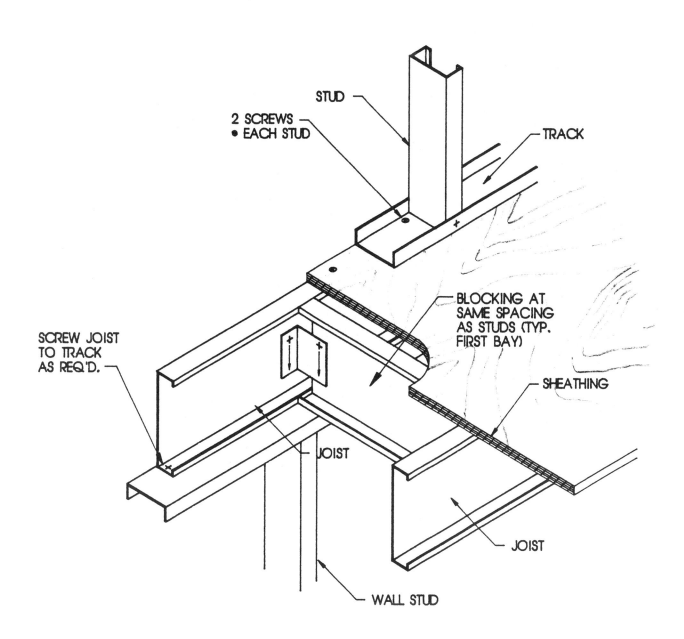

STUD

2 SCREWS • EACH STUD

TRACK

BLOCKING AT SAME SPACING AS STUDS (TYP. FIRST BAY)

SCREW JOIST TO TRACK AS REQ'D.

SHEATHING

JOIST

JOIST

WALL STUD

FLOOR JOISTS PARALLEL TO EXTERIOR WALL

**E.7**

# E. DETAILS AT EXTERIOR WALLS

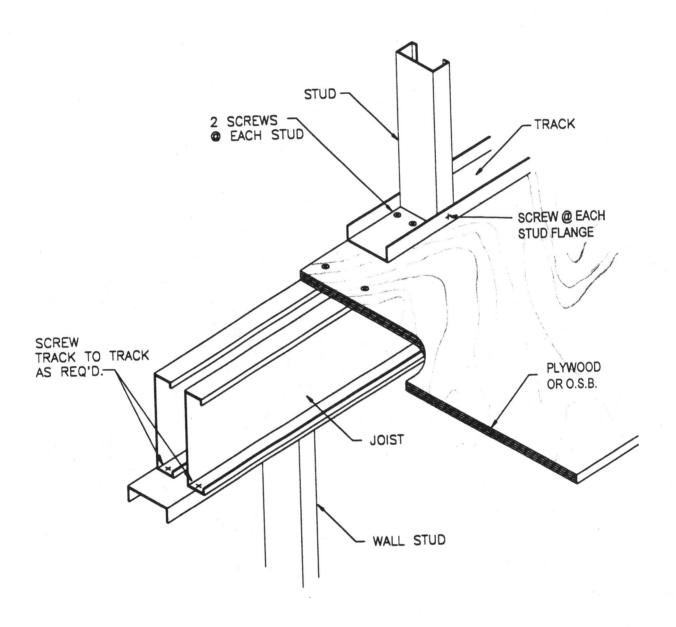

STUD

2 SCREWS
@ EACH STUD

TRACK

SCREW @ EACH
STUD FLANGE

SCREW
TRACK TO TRACK
AS REQ'D.

PLYWOOD
OR O.S.B.

JOIST

WALL STUD

**E.7a**    FLOOR JOISTS PARALLEL TO EXTERIOR WALL
(ALTERNATE)

# E. DETAILS AT EXTERIOR WALLS

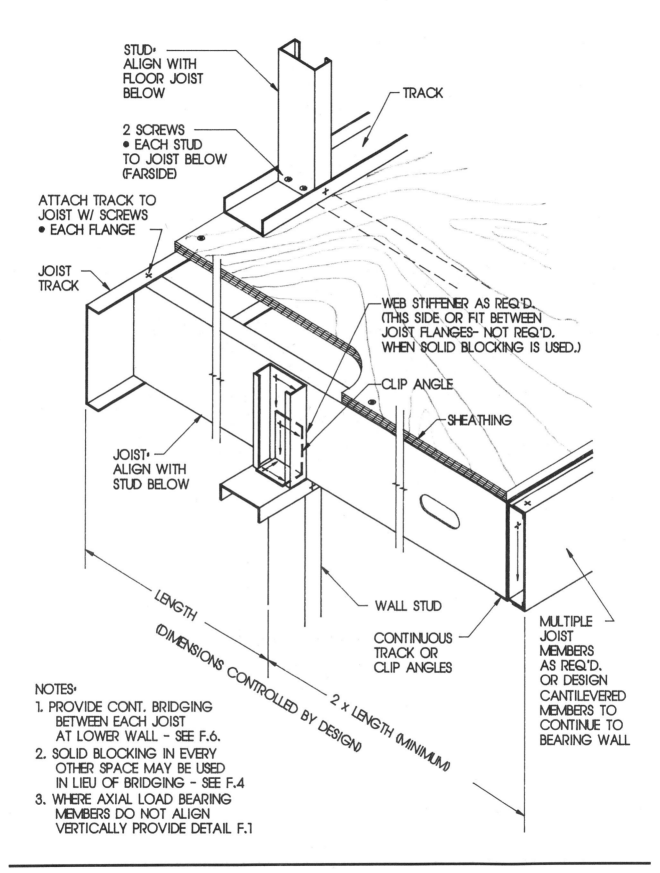

STUD·
ALIGN WITH
FLOOR JOIST
BELOW

TRACK

2 SCREWS
● EACH STUD
TO JOIST BELOW
(FARSIDE)

ATTACH TRACK TO
JOIST W/ SCREWS
● EACH FLANGE

JOIST
TRACK

WEB STIFFENER AS REQ'D.
(THIS SIDE OR FIT BETWEEN
JOIST FLANGES- NOT REQ'D.
WHEN SOLID BLOCKING IS USED.)

CLIP ANGLE

SHEATHING

JOIST·
ALIGN WITH
STUD BELOW

WALL STUD

CONTINUOUS
TRACK OR
CLIP ANGLES

MULTIPLE
JOIST
MEMBERS
AS REQ'D.
OR DESIGN
CANTILEVERED
MEMBERS TO
CONTINUE TO
BEARING WALL

LENGTH
(DIMENSIONS CONTROLLED BY DESIGN)

2 x LENGTH (MINIMUM)

NOTES·
1. PROVIDE CONT. BRIDGING
   BETWEEN EACH JOIST
   AT LOWER WALL - SEE F.6.
2. SOLID BLOCKING IN EVERY
   OTHER SPACE MAY BE USED
   IN LIEU OF BRIDGING - SEE F.4
3. WHERE AXIAL LOAD BEARING
   MEMBERS DO NOT ALIGN
   VERTICALLY PROVIDE DETAIL F.1

## FLOOR CANTILEVER

E.8

# E. DETAILS AT EXTERIOR WALLS

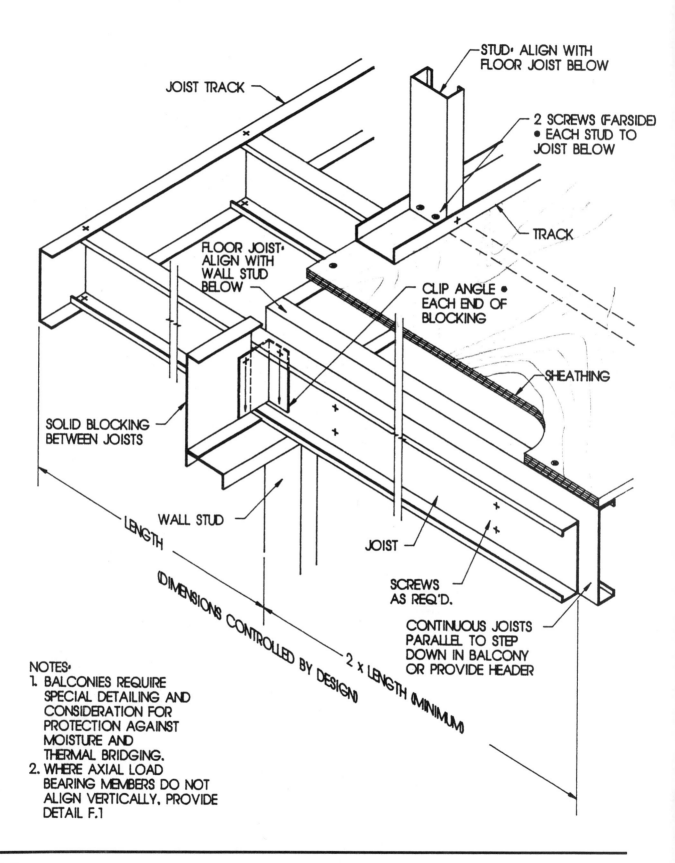

STUD· ALIGN WITH FLOOR JOIST BELOW

JOIST TRACK

2 SCREWS (FARSIDE) · EACH STUD TO JOIST BELOW

TRACK

FLOOR JOIST· ALIGN WITH WALL STUD BELOW

CLIP ANGLE · EACH END OF BLOCKING

SHEATHING

SOLID BLOCKING BETWEEN JOISTS

WALL STUD

JOIST

LENGTH

(DIMENSIONS CONTROLLED BY DESIGN)

2 x LENGTH (MINIMUM)

SCREWS AS REQ'D.

CONTINUOUS JOISTS PARALLEL TO STEP DOWN IN BALCONY OR PROVIDE HEADER

NOTES·
1. BALCONIES REQUIRE SPECIAL DETAILING AND CONSIDERATION FOR PROTECTION AGAINST MOISTURE AND THERMAL BRIDGING.
2. WHERE AXIAL LOAD BEARING MEMBERS DO NOT ALIGN VERTICALLY, PROVIDE DETAIL F.1

**E.9**            BALCONY WITH STEP DOWN

# E. DETAILS AT EXTERIOR WALLS

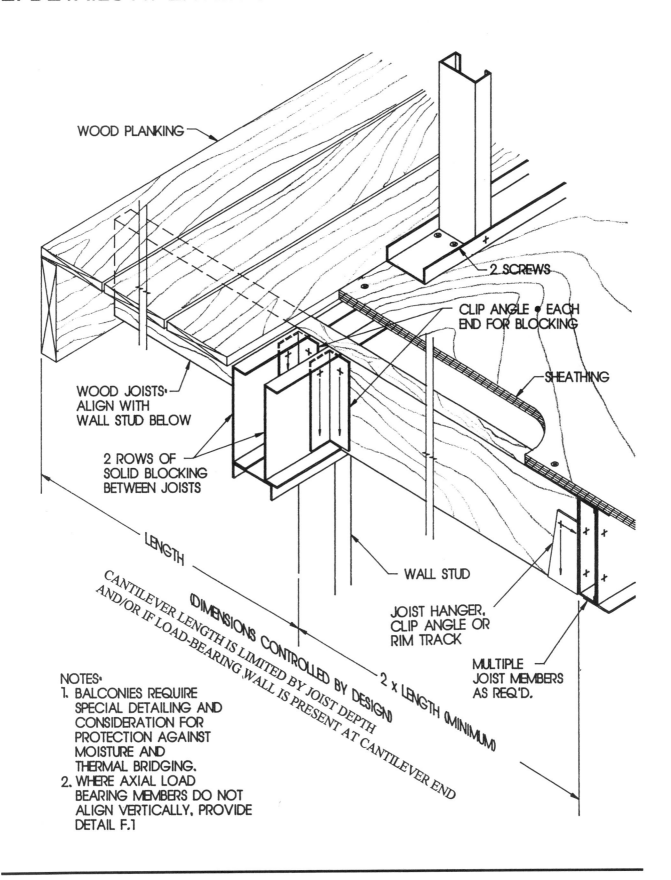

WOOD PLANKING

2 SCREWS

CLIP ANGLE • EACH
END FOR BLOCKING

SHEATHING

WOOD JOISTS•
ALIGN WITH
WALL STUD BELOW

2 ROWS OF
SOLID BLOCKING
BETWEEN JOISTS

LENGTH

(DIMENSIONS CONTROLLED BY DESIGN)

CANTILEVER LENGTH IS LIMITED BY JOIST DEPTH
AND/OR IF LOAD-BEARING WALL IS PRESENT AT CANTILEVER END

2 x LENGTH (MINIMUM)

WALL STUD

JOIST HANGER•
CLIP ANGLE OR
RIM TRACK

MULTIPLE
JOIST MEMBERS
AS REQ'D.

NOTES•
1. BALCONIES REQUIRE
SPECIAL DETAILING AND
CONSIDERATION FOR
PROTECTION AGAINST
MOISTURE AND
THERMAL BRIDGING.
2. WHERE AXIAL LOAD
BEARING MEMBERS DO NOT
ALIGN VERTICALLY, PROVIDE
DETAIL F.1

---

## WOOD DECK BALCONY

**E.10**

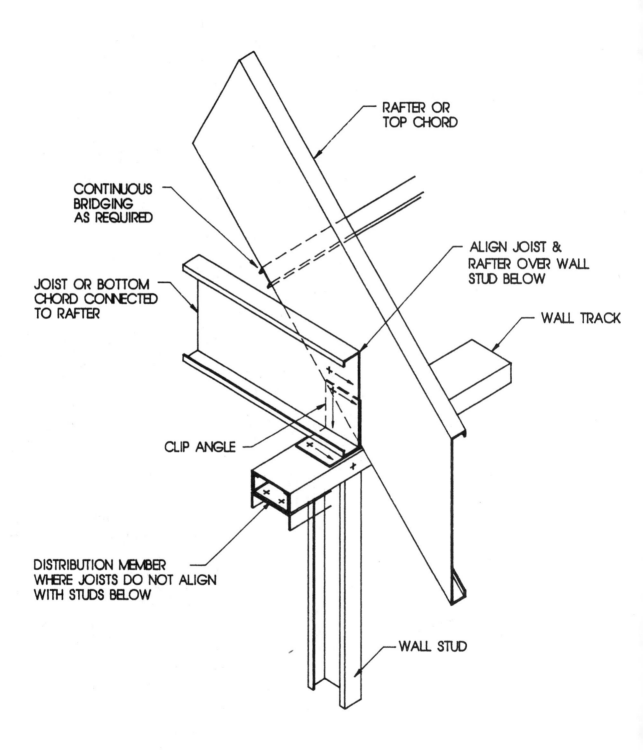

RAFTER OR
TOP CHORD

CONTINUOUS
BRIDGING
AS REQUIRED

ALIGN JOIST &
RAFTER OVER WALL
STUD BELOW

JOIST OR BOTTOM
CHORD CONNECTED
TO RAFTER

WALL TRACK

CLIP ANGLE

DISTRIBUTION MEMBER
WHERE JOISTS DO NOT ALIGN
WITH STUDS BELOW

WALL STUD

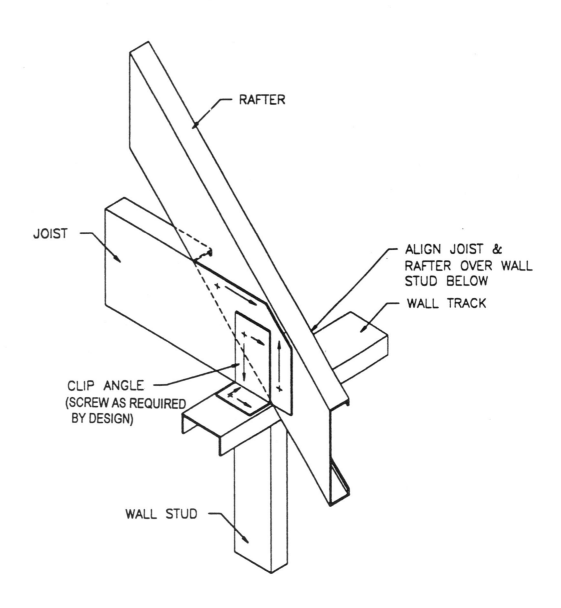

RAFTER

JOIST

ALIGN JOIST &
RAFTER OVER WALL
STUD BELOW

WALL TRACK

CLIP ANGLE
(SCREW AS REQUIRED
BY DESIGN)

WALL STUD

## ROOF TRUSS EAVE

E.12

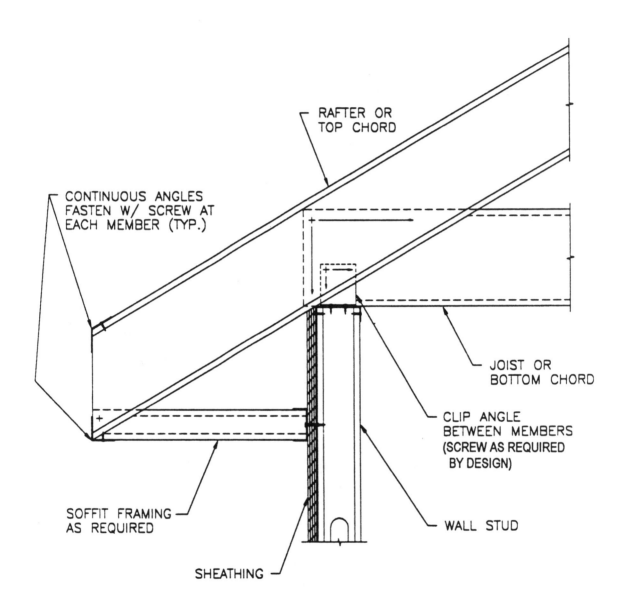

RAFTER OR
TOP CHORD

CONTINUOUS ANGLES
FASTEN W/ SCREW AT
EACH MEMBER (TYP.)

JOIST OR
BOTTOM CHORD

CLIP ANGLE
BETWEEN MEMBERS
(SCREW AS REQUIRED
BY DESIGN)

SOFFIT FRAMING
AS REQUIRED

WALL STUD

SHEATHING

# E. DETAILS AT EXTERIOR WALLS

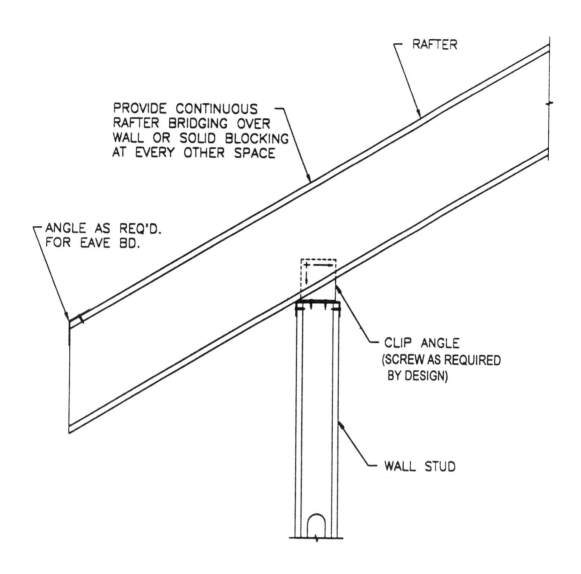

RAFTER

PROVIDE CONTINUOUS
RAFTER BRIDGING OVER
WALL OR SOLID BLOCKING
AT EVERY OTHER SPACE

ANGLE AS REQ'D.
FOR EAVE BD.

CLIP ANGLE
(SCREW AS REQUIRED
BY DESIGN)

WALL STUD

---

## ROOF EAVE AT CATHEDRAL CEILING          **E.14**

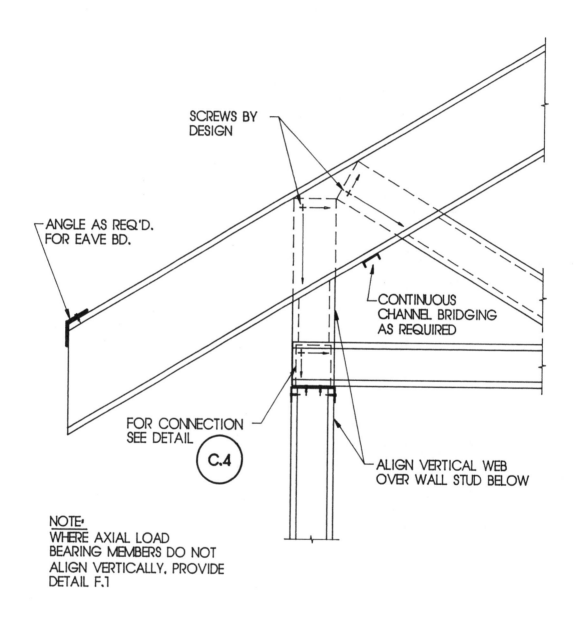

SCREWS BY
DESIGN

ANGLE AS REQ'D.
FOR EAVE BD.

CONTINUOUS
CHANNEL BRIDGING
AS REQUIRED

FOR CONNECTION
SEE DETAIL

C.4

ALIGN VERTICAL WEB
OVER WALL STUD BELOW

NOTE·
WHERE AXIAL LOAD
BEARING MEMBERS DO NOT
ALIGN VERTICALLY, PROVIDE
DETAIL F.1

# E. DETAILS AT EXTERIOR WALLS

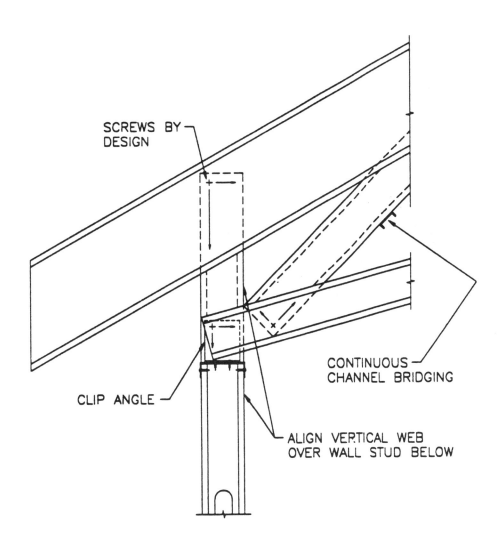

SCREWS BY
DESIGN

CLIP ANGLE

CONTINUOUS
CHANNEL BRIDGING

ALIGN VERTICAL WEB
OVER WALL STUD BELOW

---

## ROOF SCISSORS TRUSS BEARING

# E. DETAILS AT EXTERIOR WALLS

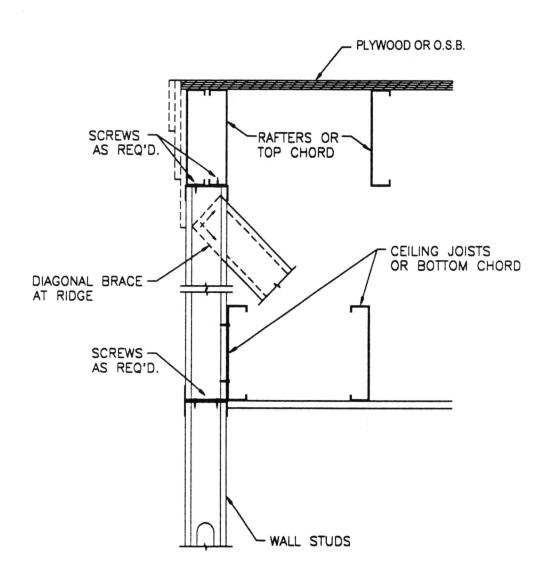

PLYWOOD OR O.S.B.

SCREWS
AS REQ'D.

RAFTERS OR
TOP CHORD

CEILING JOISTS
OR BOTTOM CHORD

DIAGONAL BRACE
AT RIDGE

SCREWS
AS REQ'D.

WALL STUDS

NOTE:
PROVIDE BRIDGING PER F.6
AT CEILING JOISTS AND RAFTERS.

**E.17**       ROOF GABLE END

# E. DETAILS AT EXTERIOR WALLS

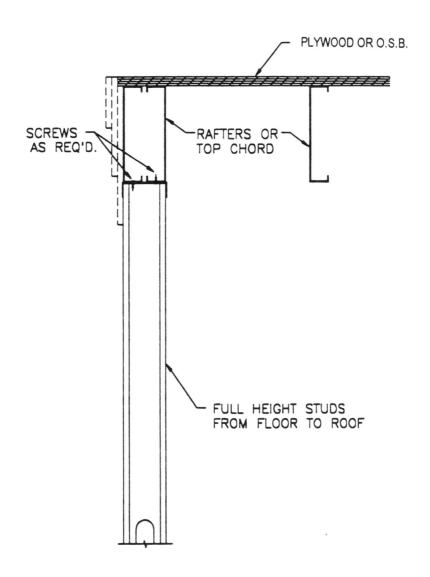

PLYWOOD OR O.S.B.

SCREWS
AS REQ'D.

RAFTERS OR
TOP CHORD

FULL HEIGHT STUDS
FROM FLOOR TO ROOF

NOTE:
PROVIDE BRIDGING PER F.6
AT CEILING JOISTS AND RAFTERS.

## ROOF GABLE END AT CATHEDRAL

# E. DETAILS AT EXTERIOR WALLS

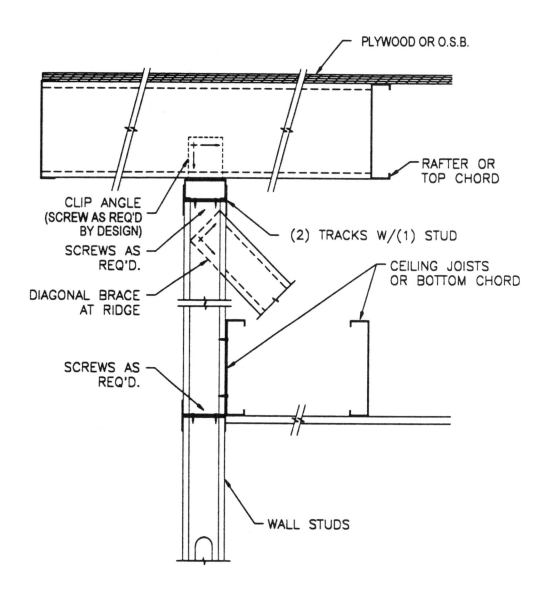

PLYWOOD OR O.S.B.

RAFTER OR
TOP CHORD

CLIP ANGLE
(SCREW AS REQ'D
BY DESIGN)

SCREWS AS
REQ'D.

DIAGONAL BRACE
AT RIDGE

(2) TRACKS W/(1) STUD

CEILING JOISTS
OR BOTTOM CHORD

SCREWS AS
REQ'D.

WALL STUDS

NOTES:
1. PROVIDE BRIDGING PER F.6
   AT CEILING JOISTS AND
   ROOF RAFTERS.
2. PROVIDE CONTINUOUS BRIDGING
   BETWEEN RAFTERS AT WALL PER F.6

# E. DETAILS AT EXTERIOR WALLS

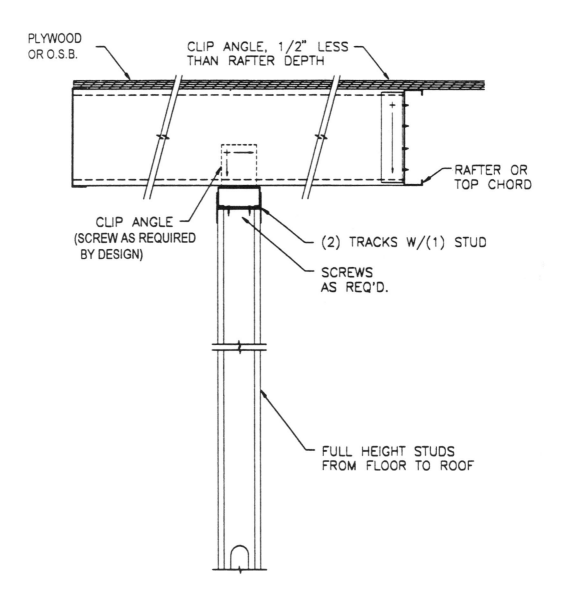

PLYWOOD OR O.S.B.

CLIP ANGLE, 1/2" LESS THAN RAFTER DEPTH

RAFTER OR TOP CHORD

CLIP ANGLE (SCREW AS REQUIRED BY DESIGN)

(2) TRACKS W/(1) STUD

SCREWS AS REQ'D.

FULL HEIGHT STUDS FROM FLOOR TO ROOF

NOTES:
1. PROVIDE BRIDGING PER F.6 AT CEILING JOISTS AND ROOF RAFTERS.
2. PROVIDE CONTINUOUS BRIDGING BETWEEN RAFTERS AT WALL PER F.6

---

## CANTILEVERED GABLE END AT CATHEDRAL          E.20

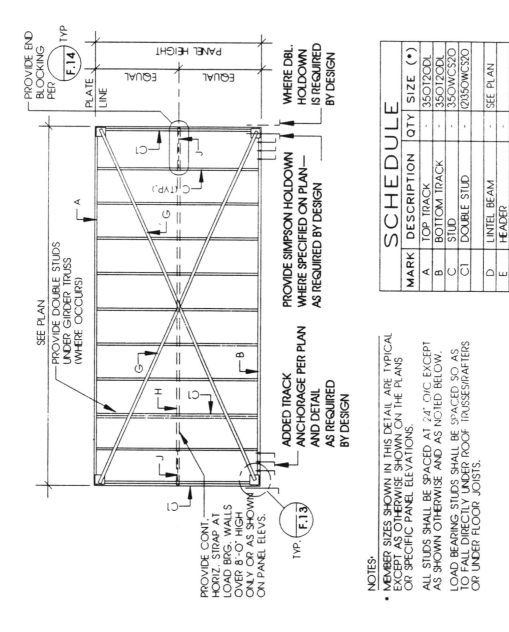

## SCHEDULE

| MARK | DESCRIPTION | QTY | SIZE (*) |
|---|---|---|---|
| A | TOP TRACK | - | 350T20L |
| B | BOTTOM TRACK | - | 350T20L |
| C | STUD | - | 350WCS20 |
| C1 | DOUBLE STUD | - | (2)350WCS20 |
| D | LINTEL BEAM | - | SEE PLAN |
| E | HEADER | - | 350T20 |
| F | SILL | - | SEE DETAIL |
| G | STRAP | - | 2"x16 GA. |
| H | STRAP | - | 350B20 |
| J | BLOCKING | - | 350B20 |
| K | LINTEL TRACK | - | 350T20 |

NOTES:

- MEMBER SIZES SHOWN IN THIS DETAIL ARE TYPICAL EXCEPT AS OTHERWISE SHOWN ON THE PLANS OR SPECIFIC PANEL ELEVATIONS.

  ALL STUDS SHALL BE SPACED AT 24" O/C EXCEPT AS SHOWN OTHERWISE AND AS NOTED BELOW.

  LOAD BEARING STUDS SHALL BE SPACED SO AS TO FALL DIRECTLY UNDER ROOF TRUSSES/RAFTERS OR UNDER FLOOR JOISTS.

# E. DETAILS AT EXTERIOR WALLS

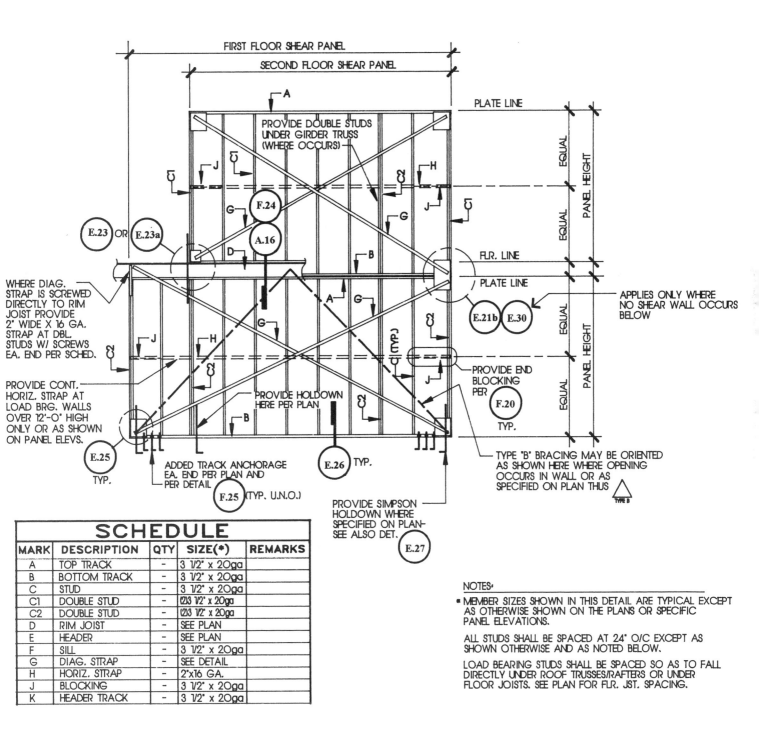

FIRST FLOOR SHEAR PANEL

SECOND FLOOR SHEAR PANEL

A

PROVIDE DOUBLE STUDS
UNDER GIRDER TRUSS
(WHERE OCCURS)

PLATE LINE

EQUAL

PANEL HEIGHT

EQUAL

E.23 OR E.23a

F.24

A.16

FLR. LINE

PLATE LINE

E.21b E.30

APPLIES ONLY WHERE
NO SHEAR WALL OCCURS
BELOW

WHERE DIAG.
STRAP IS SCREWED
DIRECTLY TO RIM
JOIST PROVIDE
2" WIDE X 16 GA.
STRAP AT DBL.
STUDS W/ SCREWS
EA. END PER SCHED.

EQUAL

PANEL HEIGHT

EQUAL

PROVIDE CONT.
HORIZ. STRAP AT
LOAD BRG. WALLS
OVER 12'-0" HIGH
ONLY OR AS SHOWN
ON PANEL ELEVS.

PROVIDE HOLDOWN
HERE PER PLAN

PROVIDE END
BLOCKING
PER

F.20

TYP.

E.25

TYP.

ADDED TRACK ANCHORAGE
EA. END PER PLAN AND
PER DETAIL

F.25 (TYP. U.N.O.)

E.26 TYP.

TYPE "B" BRACING MAY BE ORIENTED
AS SHOWN HERE WHERE OPENING
OCCURS IN WALL OR AS
SPECIFIED ON PLAN THUS

TYPE B

PROVIDE SIMPSON
HOLDOWN WHERE
SPECIFIED ON PLAN-
SEE ALSO DET.

E.27

## SCHEDULE

| MARK | DESCRIPTION | QTY | SIZE(*) | REMARKS |
|------|-------------|-----|---------|---------|
| A | TOP TRACK | - | 3 1/2" x 20ga | |
| B | BOTTOM TRACK | - | 3 1/2" x 20ga | |
| C | STUD | - | 3 1/2" x 20ga | |
| C1 | DOUBLE STUD | - | (2)3 1/2" x 20ga | |
| C2 | DOUBLE STUD | - | (2)3 1/2" x 20ga | |
| D | RIM JOIST | - | SEE PLAN | |
| E | HEADER | - | SEE PLAN | |
| F | SILL | - | 3 1/2" x 20ga | |
| G | DIAG. STRAP | - | SEE DETAIL | |
| H | HORIZ. STRAP | - | 2"x16 GA. | |
| J | BLOCKING | - | 3 1/2" x 20ga | |
| K | HEADER TRACK | - | 3 1/2" x 20ga | |

NOTES:

* MEMBER SIZES SHOWN IN THIS DETAIL ARE TYPICAL EXCEPT
AS OTHERWISE SHOWN ON THE PLANS OR SPECIFIC
PANEL ELEVATIONS.

ALL STUDS SHALL BE SPACED AT 24" O/C EXCEPT AS
SHOWN OTHERWISE AND AS NOTED BELOW.

LOAD BEARING STUDS SHALL BE SPACED SO AS TO FALL
DIRECTLY UNDER ROOF TRUSSES/RAFTERS OR UNDER
FLOOR JOISTS. SEE PLAN FOR FLR. JST. SPACING.

## TYPICAL SHEAR PANEL ELEVATION –
## 2 STORY

**E.21b**

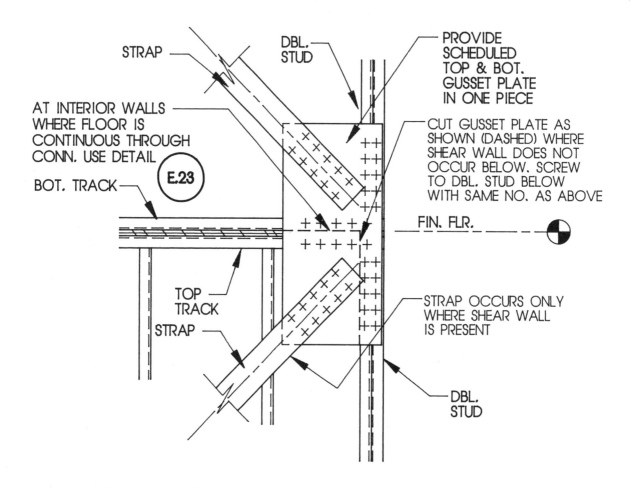

STRAP

DBL. STUD

PROVIDE SCHEDULED TOP & BOT. GUSSET PLATE IN ONE PIECE

AT INTERIOR WALLS WHERE FLOOR IS CONTINUOUS THROUGH CONN. USE DETAIL

E.23

BOT. TRACK

CUT GUSSET PLATE AS SHOWN (DASHED) WHERE SHEAR WALL DOES NOT OCCUR BELOW. SCREW TO DBL. STUD BELOW WITH SAME NO. AS ABOVE

FIN. FLR.

TOP TRACK

STRAP

STRAP OCCURS ONLY WHERE SHEAR WALL IS PRESENT

DBL. STUD

**E.22**     **STACKED SECOND FLOOR SHEAR WALL WITH COMMON GUSSET PLATE**

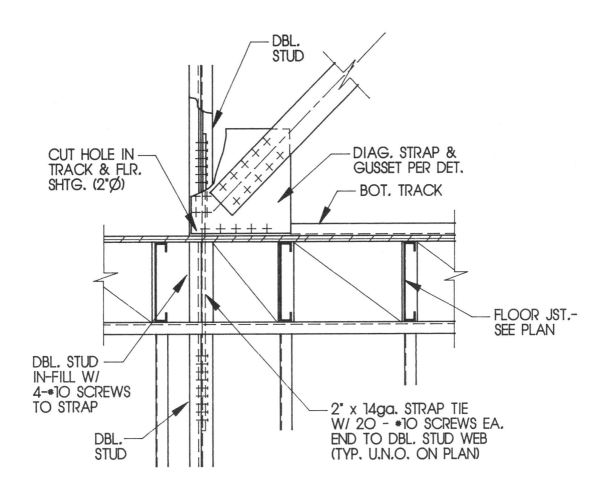

DBL.
STUD

CUT HOLE IN
TRACK & FLR.
SHTG. (2"∅)

DIAG. STRAP &
GUSSET PER DET.

BOT. TRACK

FLOOR JST.-
SEE PLAN

DBL. STUD
IN-FILL W/
4-#10 SCREWS
TO STRAP

DBL.
STUD

2" x 14ga. STRAP TIE
W/ 20 - #10 SCREWS EA.
END TO DBL. STUD WEB
(TYP. U.N.O. ON PLAN)

**SECOND FLOOR SHEAR WALL STRAP TIE**
**HOLDOWN DETAIL**

**E.23**

# E. DETAILS AT EXTERIOR WALLS

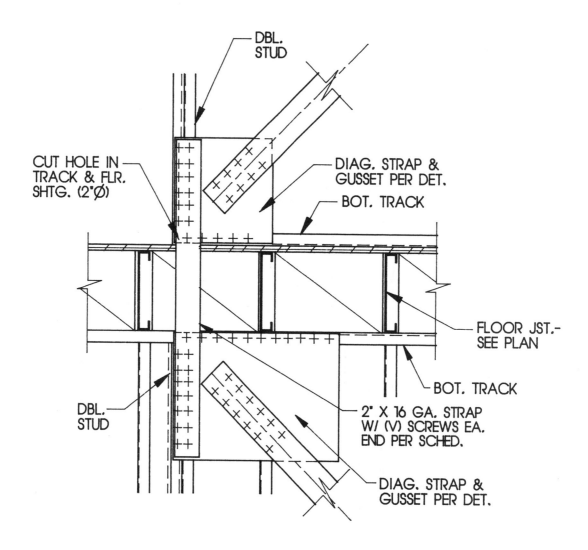

DBL. STUD

CUT HOLE IN TRACK & FLR. SHTG. (2"⌀)

DIAG. STRAP & GUSSET PER DET.

BOT. TRACK

FLOOR JST.- SEE PLAN

BOT. TRACK

DBL. STUD

2" X 16 GA. STRAP W/ (V) SCREWS EA. END PER SCHED.

DIAG. STRAP & GUSSET PER DET.

**E.23a**  SECOND FLOOR SHEAR WALL STRAP TIE
HOLDOWN DETAIL (ALTERNATE)

# E. DETAILS AT EXTERIOR WALLS

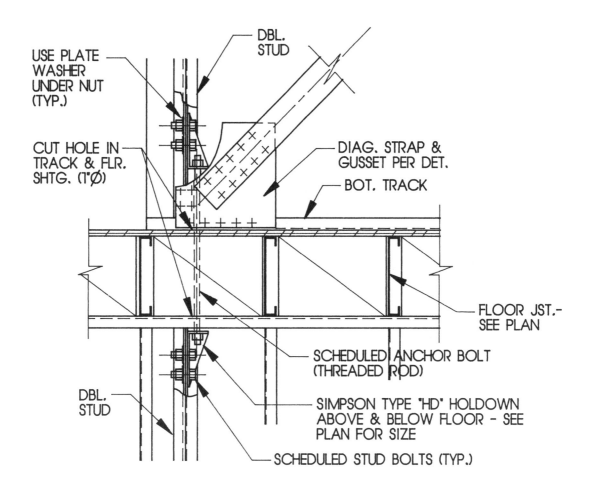

USE PLATE
WASHER
UNDER NUT
(TYP.)

DBL.
STUD

DIAG. STRAP &
GUSSET PER DET.

BOT. TRACK

CUT HOLE IN
TRACK & FLR.
SHTG. (1"Ø)

FLOOR JST.-
SEE PLAN

SCHEDULED ANCHOR BOLT
(THREADED ROD)

DBL.
STUD

SIMPSON TYPE "HD" HOLDOWN
ABOVE & BELOW FLOOR - SEE
PLAN FOR SIZE

SCHEDULED STUD BOLTS (TYP.)

SECOND FLOOR SHEAR WALL HOLDOWN DETAIL          E.24

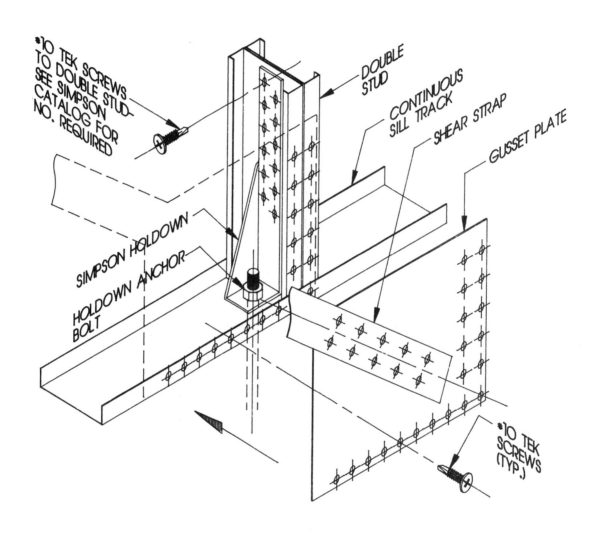

*10 TEK SCREWS TO DOUBLE STUD- SEE SIMPSON CATALOG FOR NO. REQUIRED

DOUBLE STUD

CONTINUOUS SILL TRACK

SHEAR STRAP

GUSSET PLATE

SIMPSON HOLDOWN

HOLDOWN ANCHOR BOLT

*10 TEK SCREWS (TYP.)

**E.25**

SHEAR WALL GUSSET PLATE AND
HOLDOWN ASSEMBLY

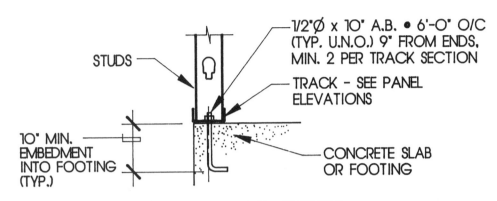

STUDS

1/2"Ø x 10" A.B. ● 6'-O" O/C
(TYP. U.N.O.) 9" FROM ENDS,
MIN. 2 PER TRACK SECTION

TRACK - SEE PANEL
ELEVATIONS

10" MIN.
EMBEDMENT
INTO FOOTING
(TYP.)

CONCRETE SLAB
OR FOOTING

## ANCHOR BOLT DETAIL

NOTE:
POWDER DRIVEN FASTENERS
CANNOT BE USED IN A
TWO POUR SYSTEM.

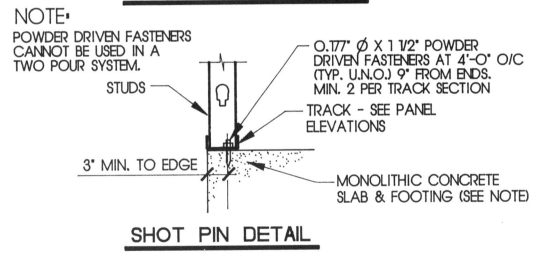

STUDS

0.177" Ø X 1 1/2" POWDER
DRIVEN FASTENERS AT 4'-O" O/C
(TYP. U.N.O.) 9" FROM ENDS.
MIN. 2 PER TRACK SECTION

TRACK - SEE PANEL
ELEVATIONS

3" MIN. TO EDGE

MONOLITHIC CONCRETE
SLAB & FOOTING (SEE NOTE)

## SHOT PIN DETAIL

---

## TYPICAL TRACK ANCHORAGE DETAIL
## AT EXTERIOR WALL ON SLAB

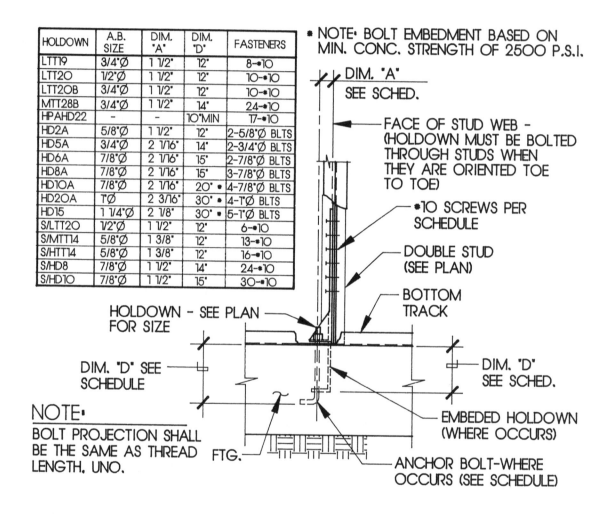

| HOLDOWN | A.B. SIZE | DIM. "A" | DIM. "D" | FASTENERS |
|---------|-----------|----------|----------|-----------|
| LTT19 | 3/4"Ø | 1 1/2" | 12" | 8-#10 |
| LTT20 | 1/2"Ø | 1 1/2" | 12" | 10-#10 |
| LTT20B | 3/4"Ø | 1 1/2" | 12" | 10-#10 |
| MTT28B | 3/4"Ø | 1 1/2" | 14" | 24-#10 |
| HPAHD22 | - | - | 10"MIN | 17-#10 |
| HD2A | 5/8"Ø | 1 1/2" | 12" | 2-5/8"Ø BLTS |
| HD5A | 3/4"Ø | 2 1/16" | 14" | 2-3/4"Ø BLTS |
| HD6A | 7/8"Ø | 2 1/16" | 15" | 2-7/8"Ø BLTS |
| HD8A | 7/8"Ø | 2 1/16" | 15" | 3-7/8"Ø BLTS |
| HD10A | 7/8"Ø | 2 1/16" | 20" * | 4-7/8"Ø BLTS |
| HD20A | 1"Ø | 2 3/16" | 30" * | 4-1"Ø BLTS |
| HD15 | 1 1/4"Ø | 2 1/8" | 30" * | 5-1"Ø BLTS |
| S/LTT20 | 1/2"Ø | 1 1/2" | 12" | 6-#10 |
| S/MTT14 | 5/8"Ø | 1 3/8" | 12" | 13-#10 |
| S/HTT14 | 5/8"Ø | 1 3/8" | 12" | 16-#10 |
| S/HD8 | 7/8"Ø | 1 1/2" | 14" | 24-#10 |
| S/HD10 | 7/8"Ø | 1 1/2" | 15" | 30-#10 |

\* NOTE: BOLT EMBEDMENT BASED ON MIN. CONC. STRENGTH OF 2500 P.S.I.

DIM. "A" SEE SCHED.

FACE OF STUD WEB – (HOLDOWN MUST BE BOLTED THROUGH STUDS WHEN THEY ARE ORIENTED TOE TO TOE)

#10 SCREWS PER SCHEDULE

DOUBLE STUD (SEE PLAN)

BOTTOM TRACK

HOLDOWN - SEE PLAN FOR SIZE

DIM. "D" SEE SCHEDULE

DIM. "D" SEE SCHED.

EMBEDED HOLDOWN (WHERE OCCURS)

ANCHOR BOLT-WHERE OCCURS (SEE SCHEDULE)

FTG.

NOTE:
BOLT PROJECTION SHALL BE THE SAME AS THREAD LENGTH, UNO.

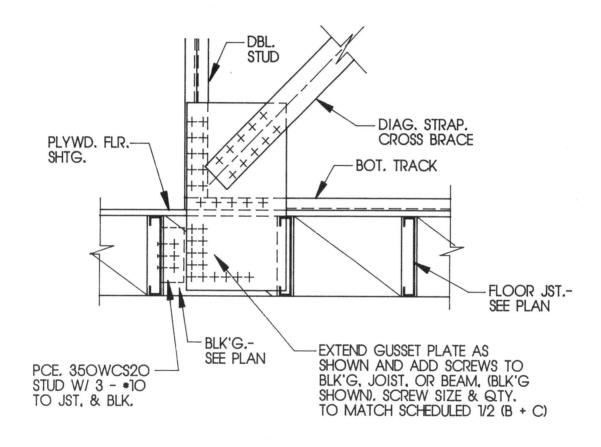

DBL.
STUD

DIAG. STRAP.
CROSS BRACE

PLYWD. FLR.
SHTG.

BOT. TRACK

FLOOR JST.-
SEE PLAN

BLK'G.-
SEE PLAN

PCE. 350WCS20
STUD W/ 3 - #10
TO JST. & BLK.

EXTEND GUSSET PLATE AS
SHOWN AND ADD SCREWS TO
BLK'G, JOIST, OR BEAM. (BLK'G
SHOWN). SCREW SIZE & QTY.
TO MATCH SCHEDULED 1/2 (B + C)

## SECOND FLOOR SHEAR HOLDOWN
## TO FLOOR JOISTS

**E.28**

# E. DETAILS AT EXTERIOR WALLS

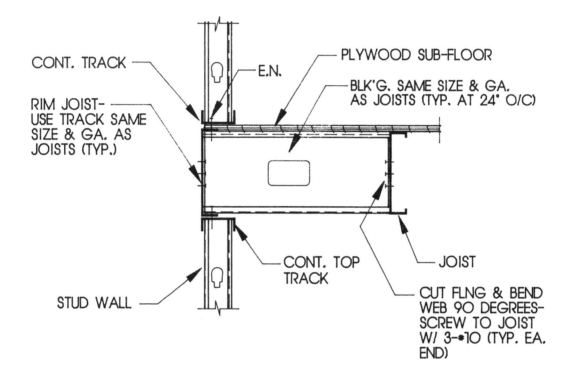

CONT. TRACK

E.N.

PLYWOOD SUB-FLOOR

BLK'G. SAME SIZE & GA. AS JOISTS (TYP. AT 24" O/C)

RIM JOIST- USE TRACK SAME SIZE & GA. AS JOISTS (TYP.)

CONT. TOP TRACK

JOIST

STUD WALL

CUT FLNG & BEND WEB 90 DEGREES- SCREW TO JOIST W/ 3-#10 (TYP. EA. END)

**E.29**

**EXTERIOR WALL SECTION WITH PARALLEL FLOOR JOISTS**

# E. DETAILS AT EXTERIOR WALLS

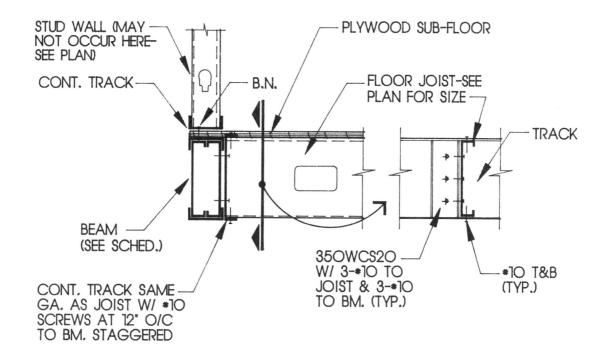

STUD WALL (MAY NOT OCCUR HERE-SEE PLAN)

PLYWOOD SUB-FLOOR

CONT. TRACK

B.N.

FLOOR JOIST-SEE PLAN FOR SIZE

TRACK

BEAM (SEE SCHED.)

CONT. TRACK SAME GA. AS JOIST W/ #10 SCREWS AT 12" O/C TO BM. STAGGERED

350WCS20 W/ 3-#10 TO JOIST & 3-#10 TO BM. (TYP.)

#10 T&B (TYP.)

**FLOOR JOIST TO FLUSH FRAMED BEAM CONNECTION**

**E.30**

# E. DETAILS AT EXTERIOR WALLS

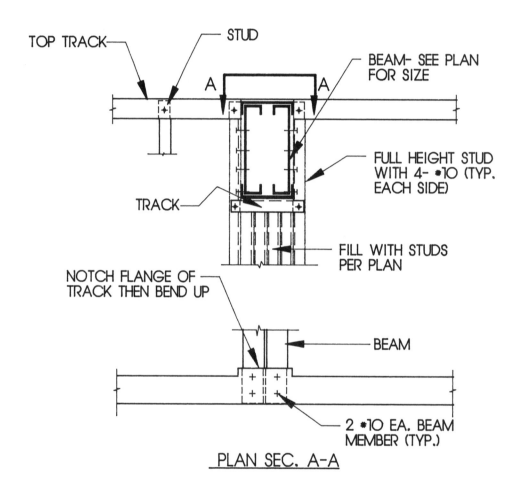

TOP TRACK

STUD

BEAM- SEE PLAN FOR SIZE

A          A

FULL HEIGHT STUD WITH 4- #10 (TYP. EACH SIDE)

TRACK

FILL WITH STUDS PER PLAN

NOTCH FLANGE OF TRACK THEN BEND UP

BEAM

2 #10 EA. BEAM MEMBER (TYP.)

PLAN SEC. A-A

TYPICAL DROPPED BEAM
TO WALL CONNECTION

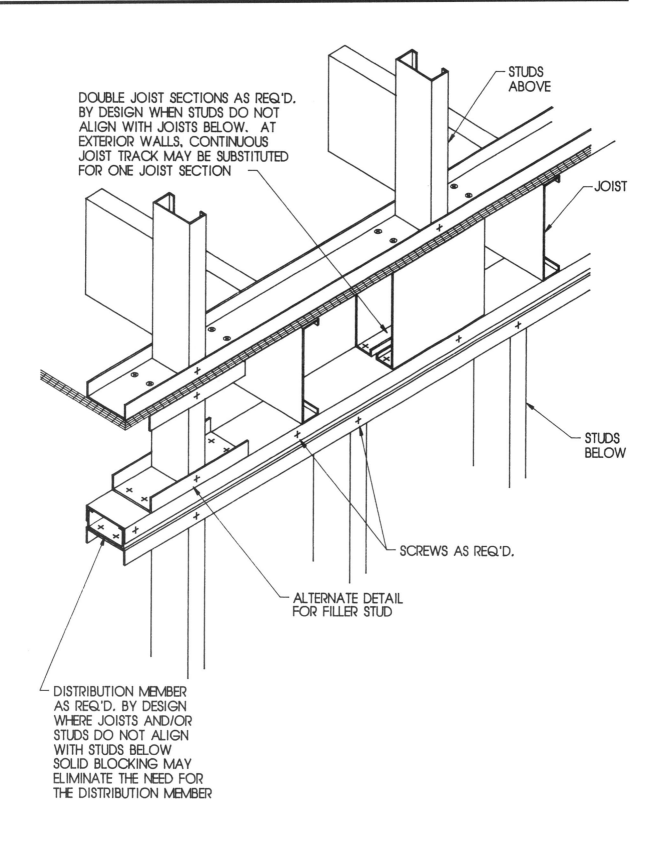

DOUBLE JOIST SECTIONS AS REQ'D.
BY DESIGN WHEN STUDS DO NOT
ALIGN WITH JOISTS BELOW. AT
EXTERIOR WALLS, CONTINUOUS
JOIST TRACK MAY BE SUBSTITUTED
FOR ONE JOIST SECTION

STUDS
ABOVE

JOIST

STUDS
BELOW

SCREWS AS REQ'D.

ALTERNATE DETAIL
FOR FILLER STUD

DISTRIBUTION MEMBER
AS REQ'D. BY DESIGN
WHERE JOISTS AND/OR
STUDS DO NOT ALIGN
WITH STUDS BELOW
SOLID BLOCKING MAY
ELIMINATE THE NEED FOR
THE DISTRIBUTION MEMBER

## TOP TRACK LOAD DISTRIBUTION DETAILS          F.1

# F. MISC. BRIDGING, BLOCKING, REINFORCEMENT, ETC.

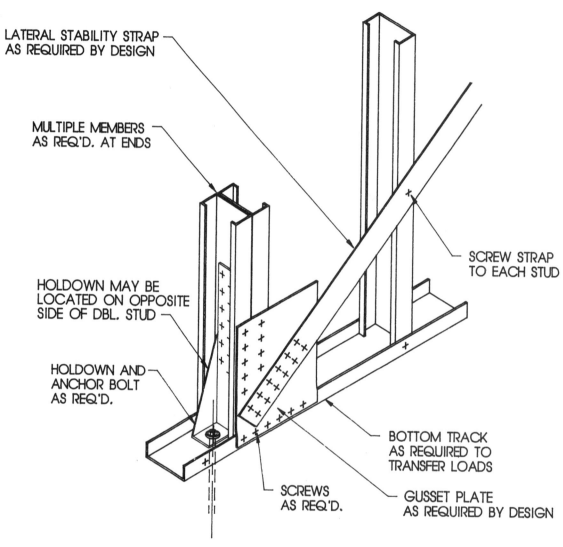

LATERAL STABILITY STRAP
AS REQUIRED BY DESIGN

MULTIPLE MEMBERS
AS REQ'D. AT ENDS

HOLDOWN MAY BE
LOCATED ON OPPOSITE
SIDE OF DBL. STUD

HOLDOWN AND
ANCHOR BOLT
AS REQ'D.

SCREW STRAP
TO EACH STUD

SCREWS
AS REQ'D.

BOTTOM TRACK
AS REQUIRED TO
TRANSFER LOADS

GUSSET PLATE
AS REQUIRED BY DESIGN

NOTE:
STRAP FORCES MAY REQUIRE
ADDITIONAL STIFFENING OF THE
BOTTOM TRACK

# F. MISC. BRIDGING, BLOCKING, REINFORCEMENT, ETC.

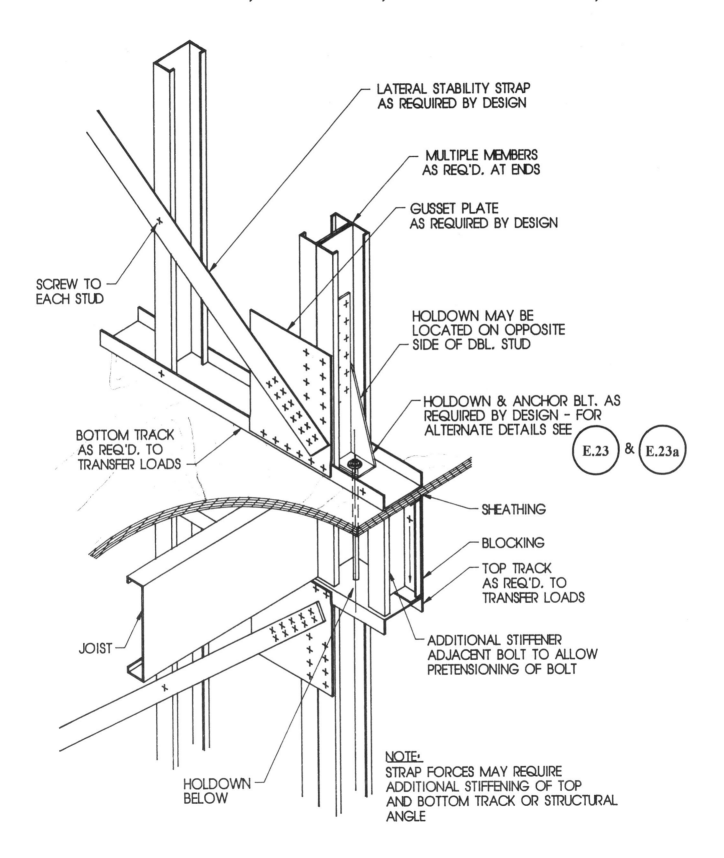

LATERAL STABILITY STRAP
AS REQUIRED BY DESIGN

MULTIPLE MEMBERS
AS REQ'D. AT ENDS

GUSSET PLATE
AS REQUIRED BY DESIGN

SCREW TO
EACH STUD

HOLDOWN MAY BE
LOCATED ON OPPOSITE
SIDE OF DBL. STUD

BOTTOM TRACK
AS REQ'D. TO
TRANSFER LOADS

HOLDOWN & ANCHOR BLT. AS
REQUIRED BY DESIGN – FOR
ALTERNATE DETAILS SEE

E.23 & E.23a

SHEATHING

BLOCKING

TOP TRACK
AS REQ'D. TO
TRANSFER LOADS

JOIST

ADDITIONAL STIFFENER
ADJACENT BOLT TO ALLOW
PRETENSIONING OF BOLT

HOLDOWN
BELOW

NOTE:
STRAP FORCES MAY REQUIRE
ADDITIONAL STIFFENING OF TOP
AND BOTTOM TRACK OR STRUCTURAL
ANGLE

SHEAR WALL HOLDOWN AT SECOND FLOOR          F.3

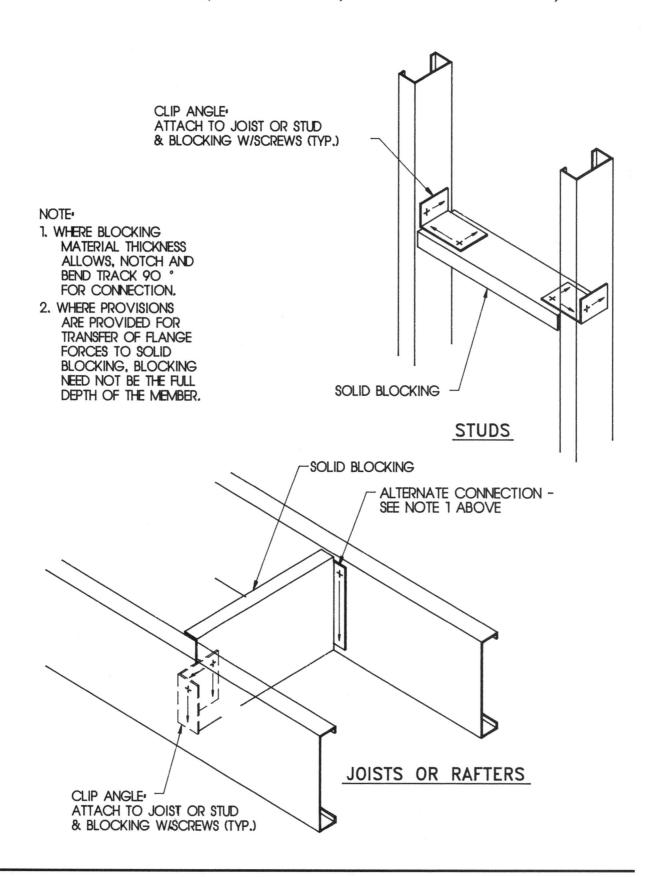

CLIP ANGLE·
ATTACH TO JOIST OR STUD
& BLOCKING W/SCREWS (TYP.)

NOTE·
1. WHERE BLOCKING
   MATERIAL THICKNESS
   ALLOWS, NOTCH AND
   BEND TRACK 90 °
   FOR CONNECTION.
2. WHERE PROVISIONS
   ARE PROVIDED FOR
   TRANSFER OF FLANGE
   FORCES TO SOLID
   BLOCKING, BLOCKING
   NEED NOT BE THE FULL
   DEPTH OF THE MEMBER.

SOLID BLOCKING

**STUDS**

SOLID BLOCKING

ALTERNATE CONNECTION –
SEE NOTE 1 ABOVE

**JOISTS OR RAFTERS**

CLIP ANGLE·
ATTACH TO JOIST OR STUD
& BLOCKING W/SCREWS (TYP.)

**F.4**          SOLID BLOCKING

# F. MISC. BRIDGING, BLOCKING, REINFORCEMENT, ETC.

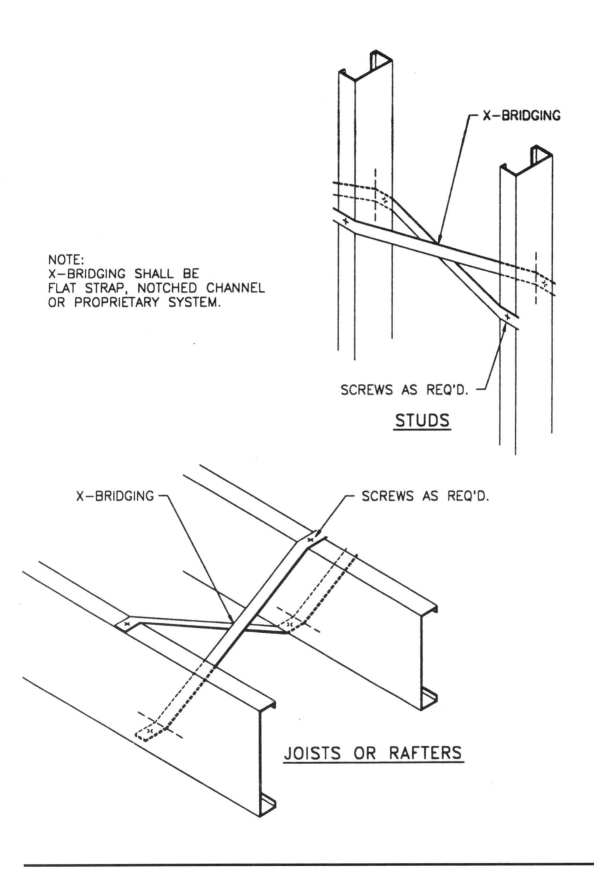

NOTE:
X—BRIDGING SHALL BE
FLAT STRAP, NOTCHED CHANNEL
OR PROPRIETARY SYSTEM.

X—BRIDGING

SCREWS AS REQ'D.

## STUDS

X—BRIDGING

SCREWS AS REQ'D.

## JOISTS OR RAFTERS

---

CROSS BRIDGING

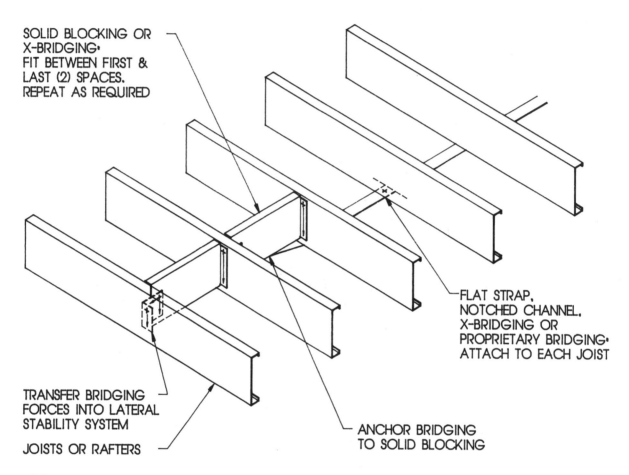

SOLID BLOCKING OR
X-BRIDGING·
FIT BETWEEN FIRST &
LAST (2) SPACES.
REPEAT AS REQUIRED

FLAT STRAP,
NOTCHED CHANNEL·
X-BRIDGING OR
PROPRIETARY BRIDGING·
ATTACH TO EACH JOIST

TRANSFER BRIDGING
FORCES INTO LATERAL
STABILITY SYSTEM

JOISTS OR RAFTERS

ANCHOR BRIDGING
TO SOLID BLOCKING

NOTE·
IF SHEATHING IS NOT INSTALLED
ON MEMBERS, BRIDGING IS
REQ'D. ON BOTH FLANGES.

# F. MISC. BRIDGING, BLOCKING, REINFORCEMENT, ETC.

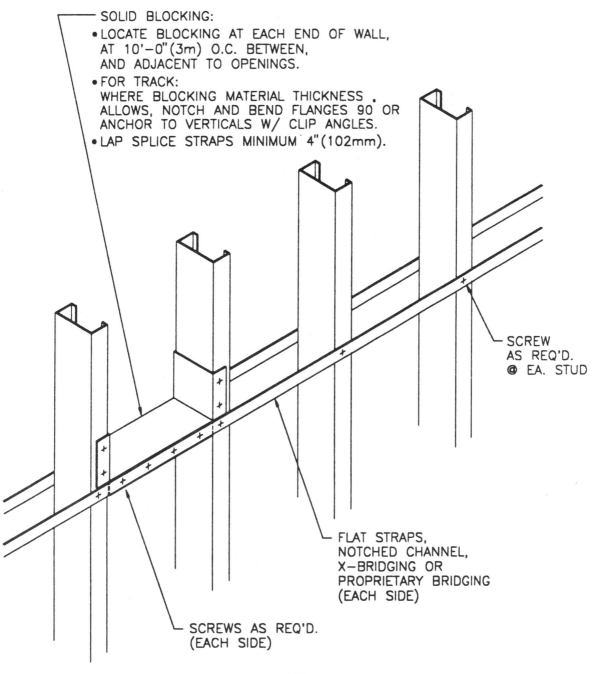

SOLID BLOCKING:
- LOCATE BLOCKING AT EACH END OF WALL, AT 10'-0"(3m) O.C. BETWEEN, AND ADJACENT TO OPENINGS.
- FOR TRACK: WHERE BLOCKING MATERIAL THICKNESS ALLOWS, NOTCH AND BEND FLANGES 90° OR ANCHOR TO VERTICALS W/ CLIP ANGLES.
- LAP SPLICE STRAPS MINIMUM 4"(102mm).

SCREW AS REQ'D. @ EA. STUD

FLAT STRAPS, NOTCHED CHANNEL, X-BRIDGING OR PROPRIETARY BRIDGING (EACH SIDE)

SCREWS AS REQ'D. (EACH SIDE)

NOTE: NUMBER OF ROWS OF BRIDGING AS REQ'D. BY DESIGN

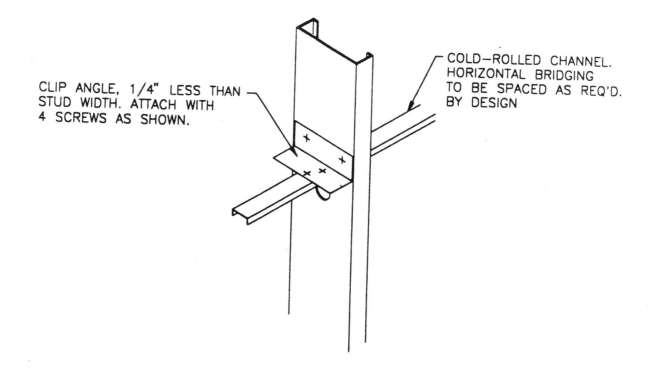

CLIP ANGLE, 1/4" LESS THAN STUD WIDTH. ATTACH WITH 4 SCREWS AS SHOWN.

COLD—ROLLED CHANNEL. HORIZONTAL BRIDGING TO BE SPACED AS REQ'D. BY DESIGN

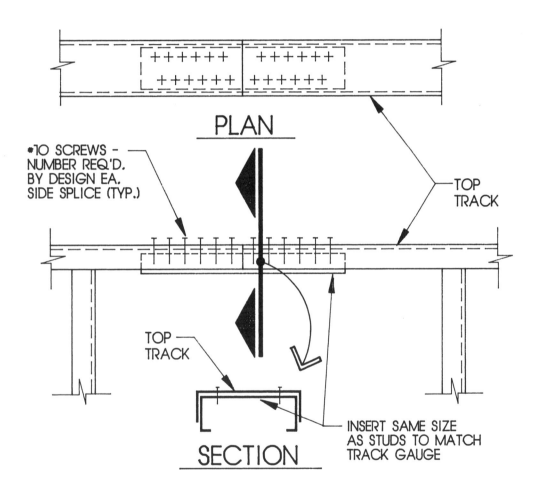

PLAN

#10 SCREWS -
NUMBER REQ'D.
BY DESIGN EA.
SIDE SPLICE (TYP.)

TOP
TRACK

TOP
TRACK

INSERT SAME SIZE
AS STUDS TO MATCH
TRACK GAUGE

SECTION

---

TOP TRACK SPLICE DETAIL          **F.9a**

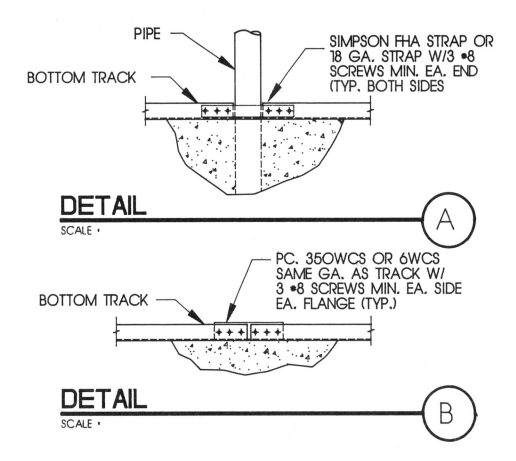

PIPE

BOTTOM TRACK

SIMPSON FHA STRAP OR
18 GA. STRAP W/3 #8
SCREWS MIN. EA. END
(TYP. BOTH SIDES

**DETAIL**
SCALE :

A

PC. 350WCS OR 6WCS
SAME GA. AS TRACK W/
3 #8 SCREWS MIN. EA. SIDE
EA. FLANGE (TYP.)

BOTTOM TRACK

**DETAIL**
SCALE :

B

# F. MISC. BRIDGING, BLOCKING, REINFORCEMENT, ETC.

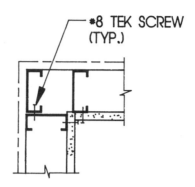

#8 TEK SCREW
(TYP.)

---

**F.10**        TYPICAL EXTERIOR CORNER FRAMING        **F.10**

---

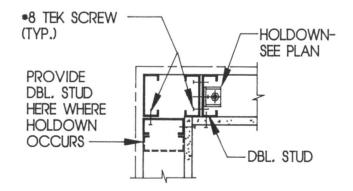

#8 TEK SCREW
(TYP.)

HOLDOWN-
SEE PLAN

PROVIDE
DBL. STUD
HERE WHERE
HOLDOWN
OCCURS

DBL. STUD

---

EXTERIOR CORNER FRAMING WITH HOLDOWN        **F.10a**

# F. MISC. BRIDGING, BLOCKING, REINFORCEMENT, ETC.

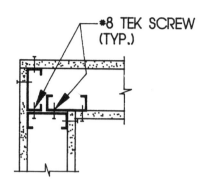

| | | |
|---|---|---|
| **F.10b** | TYPICAL INTERIOR CORNER FRAMING | **F.10b** |

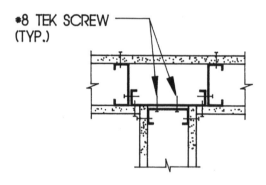

| | | |
|---|---|---|
| **F.11** | TYPICAL INTERIOR INTERSECTION | **F.11** |

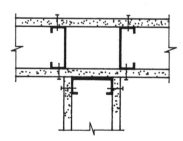

**F.11a**  ALTERNATE INTERIOR INTERSECTION FRAMING

# F. MISC. BRIDGING, BLOCKING, REINFORCEMENT, ETC.

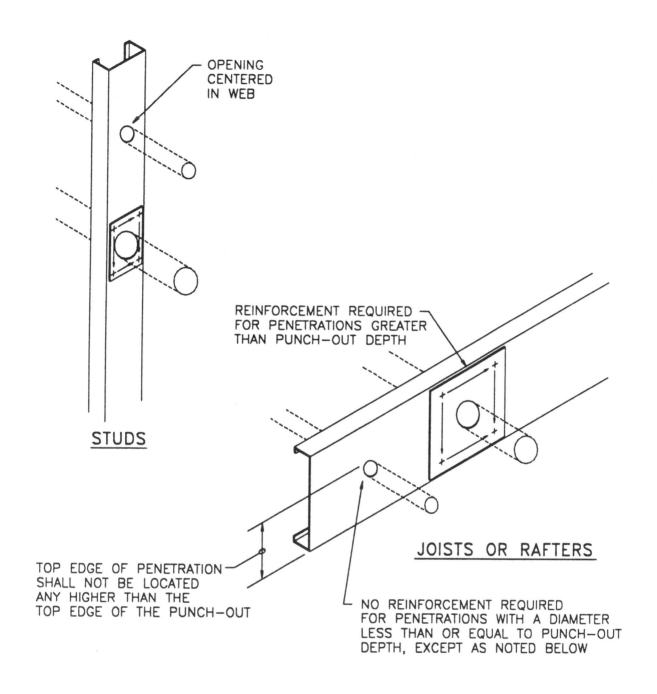

OPENING CENTERED IN WEB

STUDS

REINFORCEMENT REQUIRED FOR PENETRATIONS GREATER THAN PUNCH-OUT DEPTH

JOISTS OR RAFTERS

TOP EDGE OF PENETRATION SHALL NOT BE LOCATED ANY HIGHER THAN THE TOP EDGE OF THE PUNCH-OUT

NO REINFORCEMENT REQUIRED FOR PENETRATIONS WITH A DIAMETER LESS THAN OR EQUAL TO PUNCH-OUT DEPTH, EXCEPT AS NOTED BELOW

NOTES:
1. FLANGES SHALL NOT BE NOTCHED OR CUT.
2. CAPACITY VERIFICATION BY DESIGN IS REQ'D. FOR ANY OPENINGS LOCATED AT CONCENTRATED LOADS AND BEARING ENDS.

JOIST, STUD OR RAFTER WEB PENETRATIONS       F.12

# F. MISC. BRIDGING, BLOCKING, REINFORCEMENT, ETC.

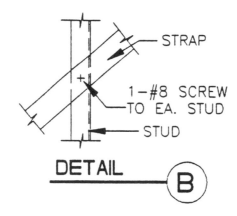

STRAP

1-#8 SCREW
TO EA. STUD

STUD

**DETAIL** (B)

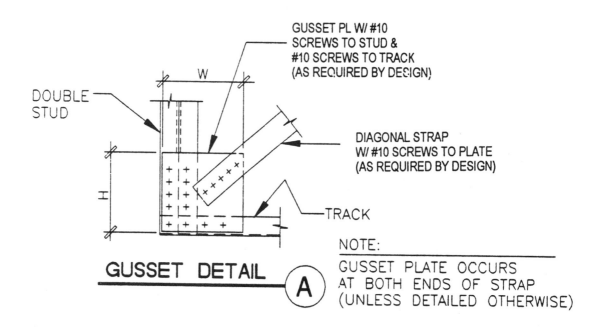

GUSSET PL W/ #10
SCREWS TO STUD &
#10 SCREWS TO TRACK
(AS REQUIRED BY DESIGN)

W

DOUBLE
STUD

DIAGONAL STRAP
W/ #10 SCREWS TO PLATE
(AS REQUIRED BY DESIGN)

H

TRACK

**GUSSET DETAIL** (A)

NOTE:
GUSSET PLATE OCCURS
AT BOTH ENDS OF STRAP
(UNLESS DETAILED OTHERWISE)

# F. MISC. BRIDGING, BLOCKING, REINFORCEMENT, ETC.

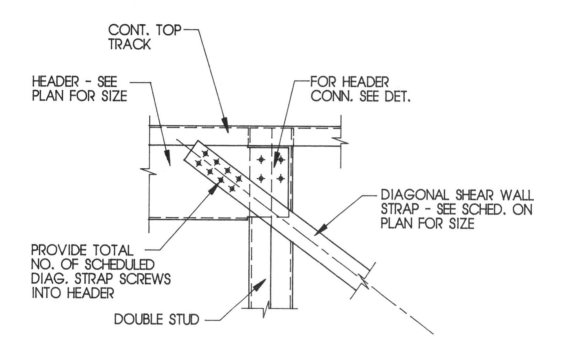

CONT. TOP TRACK

HEADER – SEE PLAN FOR SIZE

FOR HEADER CONN. SEE DET.

DIAGONAL SHEAR WALL STRAP – SEE SCHED. ON PLAN FOR SIZE

PROVIDE TOTAL NO. OF SCHEDULED DIAG. STRAP SCREWS INTO HEADER

DOUBLE STUD

DIAGONAL STRAP ATTACHMENT TO HEADER

**F.13a**

# F. MISC. BRIDGING, BLOCKING, REINFORCEMENT, ETC.

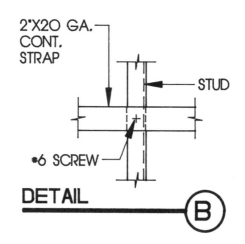

2"X20 GA. CONT. STRAP

STUD

*6 SCREW

**DETAIL** Ⓑ

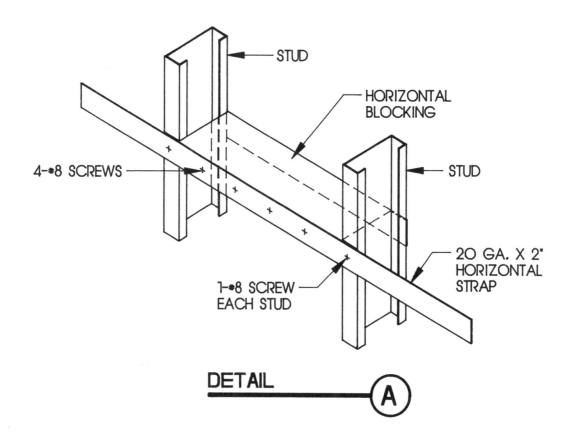

STUD

HORIZONTAL BLOCKING

4-*8 SCREWS

STUD

20 GA. X 2" HORIZONTAL STRAP

1-*8 SCREW EACH STUD

**DETAIL** Ⓐ

**F.14**    WALL HORIZONTAL BLOCKING / BRIDGING DETAIL

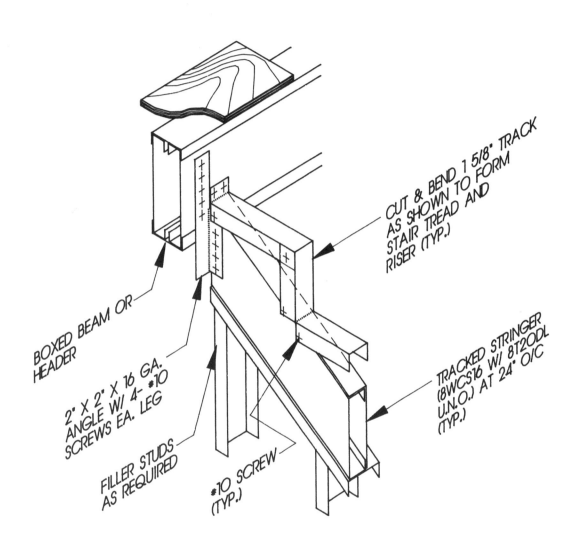

CUT & BEND 1 5/8" TRACK AS SHOWN TO FORM STAIR TREAD AND RISER (TYP.)

BOXED BEAM OR HEADER

2" X 2" X 16 GA. ANGLE W/ 4- #10 SCREWS EA. LEG

TRACKED STRINGER (8WCS16 W/ 8T20DL U.N.O.) AT 24" O/C (TYP.)

FILLER STUDS AS REQUIRED

#10 SCREW (TYP.)

---

**TYPICAL STAIR STRINGER CONNECTION**     **F.15**

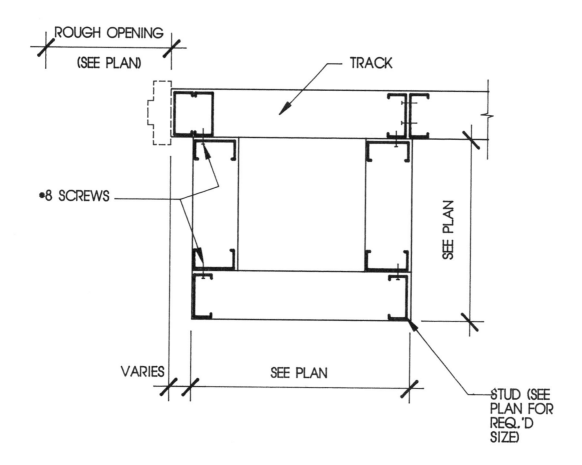

ROUGH OPENING
(SEE PLAN)

TRACK

*8 SCREWS

SEE PLAN

VARIES

SEE PLAN

STUD (SEE PLAN FOR REQ.'D SIZE)

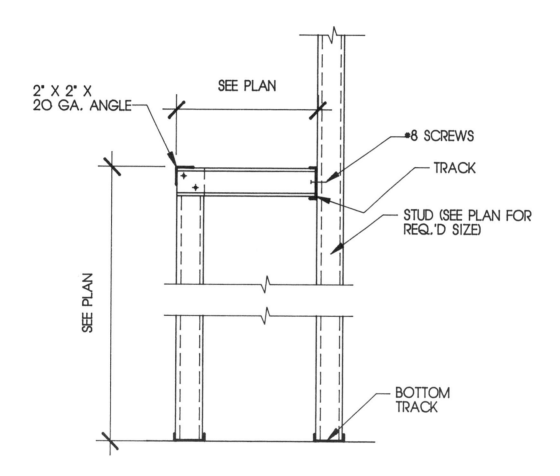

2" X 2" X
20 GA. ANGLE

SEE PLAN

SEE PLAN

#8 SCREWS

TRACK

STUD (SEE PLAN FOR
REQ.'D SIZE)

BOTTOM
TRACK

TYPICAL POT SHELF DETAIL                                    **F.17**

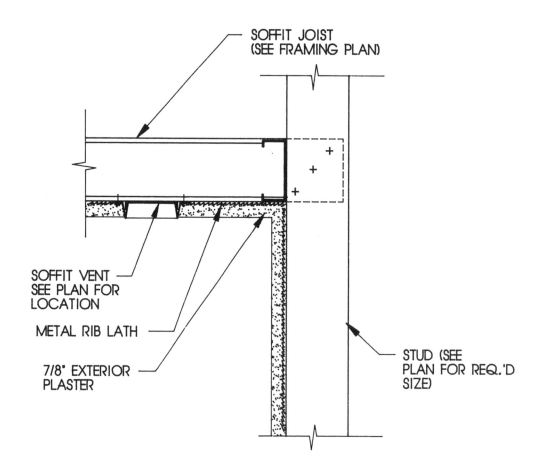

SOFFIT JOIST
(SEE FRAMING PLAN)

SOFFIT VENT
SEE PLAN FOR
LOCATION

METAL RIB LATH

7/8" EXTERIOR
PLASTER

STUD (SEE
PLAN FOR REQ.'D
SIZE)

**F.18**   TYPICAL PLASTER SOFFIT DETAIL

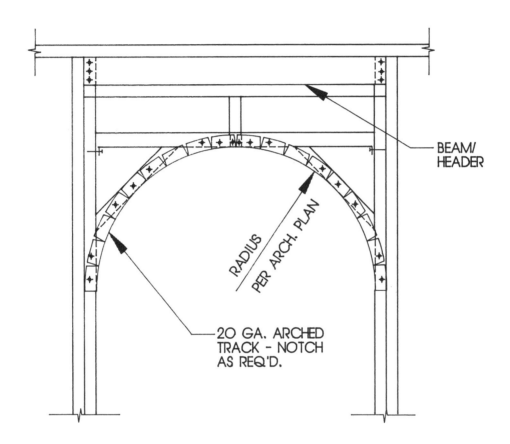

BEAM/
HEADER

RADIUS
PER ARCH. PLAN

20 GA. ARCHED
TRACK - NOTCH
AS REQ'D.

TYPICAL ARCH OPENING DETAIL     **F.19**

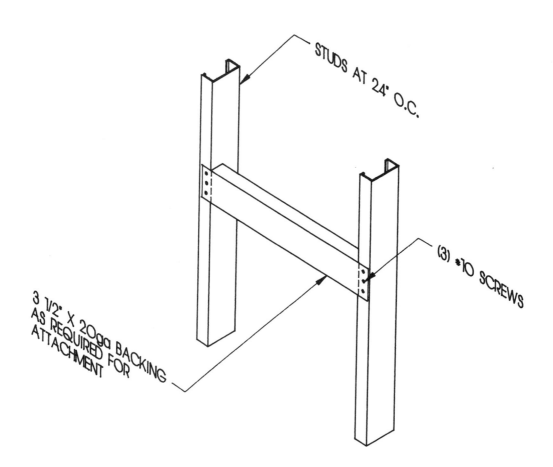

STUDS AT 24" O.C.

(3) #10 SCREWS

3 1/2" X 20ga BACKING
AS REQUIRED FOR
ATTACHMENT

# F. MISC. BRIDGING, BLOCKING, REINFORCEMENT, ETC.

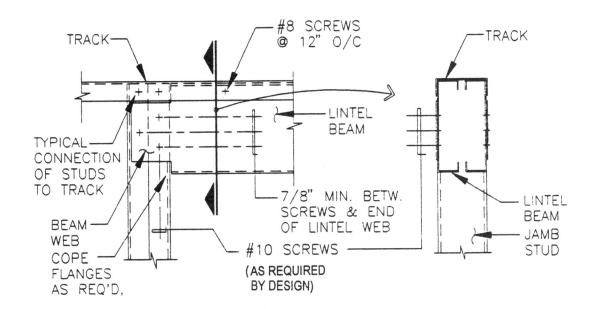

TRACK

#8 SCREWS @ 12" O/C

TRACK

LINTEL BEAM

TYPICAL CONNECTION OF STUDS TO TRACK

7/8" MIN. BETW. SCREWS & END OF LINTEL WEB

BEAM WEB COPE FLANGES AS REQ'D,

#10 SCREWS

(AS REQUIRED BY DESIGN)

LINTEL BEAM

JAMB STUD

TYPICAL LINTEL BEAM CONNECTION          **F.21**

# F. MISC. BRIDGING, BLOCKING, REINFORCEMENT, ETC.

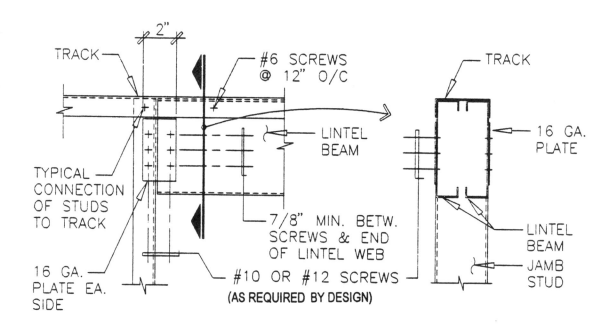

TRACK

2"

#6 SCREWS
@ 12" O/C

TRACK

LINTEL
BEAM

16 GA.
PLATE

TYPICAL
CONNECTION
OF STUDS
TO TRACK

7/8" MIN. BETW.
SCREWS & END
OF LINTEL WEB

LINTEL
BEAM

16 GA.
PLATE EA.
SIDE

#10 OR #12 SCREWS
(AS REQUIRED BY DESIGN)

JAMB
STUD

### TYPICAL LINTEL BEAM CONNECTION
### (ALTERNATE)

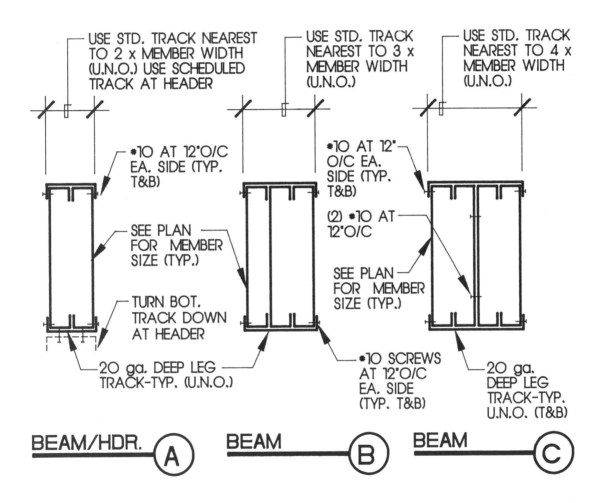

USE STD. TRACK NEAREST TO 2 x MEMBER WIDTH (U.N.O.) USE SCHEDULED TRACK AT HEADER

USE STD. TRACK NEAREST TO 3 x MEMBER WIDTH (U.N.O.)

USE STD. TRACK NEAREST TO 4 x MEMBER WIDTH (U.N.O.)

#10 AT 12"O/C EA. SIDE (TYP. T&B)

SEE PLAN FOR MEMBER SIZE (TYP.)

TURN BOT. TRACK DOWN AT HEADER

20 ga. DEEP LEG TRACK-TYP. (U.N.O.)

#10 AT 12" O/C EA. SIDE (TYP. T&B)

(2) #10 AT 12"O/C

SEE PLAN FOR MEMBER SIZE (TYP.)

#10 SCREWS AT 12"O/C EA. SIDE (TYP. T&B)

20 ga. DEEP LEG TRACK-TYP. U.N.O. (T&B)

**BEAM/HDR.** (A)    **BEAM** (B)    **BEAM** (C)

---

## TYPICAL BOXED HEADER AND BEAM DETAILS  **F.23**

# F. MISC. BRIDGING, BLOCKING, REINFORCEMENT, ETC.

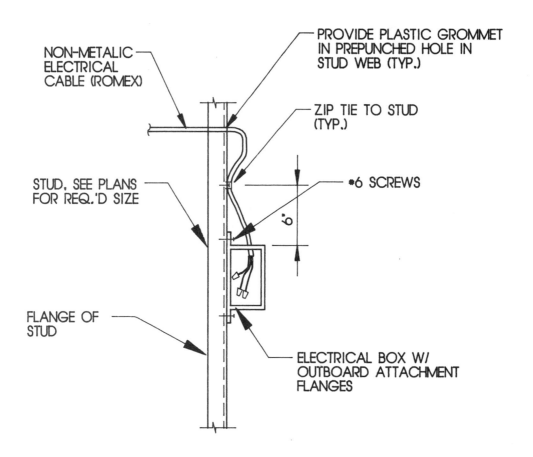

NON-METALIC
ELECTRICAL
CABLE (ROMEX)

PROVIDE PLASTIC GROMMET
IN PREPUNCHED HOLE IN
STUD WEB (TYP.)

ZIP TIE TO STUD
(TYP.)

STUD, SEE PLANS
FOR REQ.'D SIZE

#6 SCREWS

6"

FLANGE OF
STUD

ELECTRICAL BOX W/
OUTBOARD ATTACHMENT
FLANGES

# F. MISC. BRIDGING, BLOCKING, REINFORCEMENT, ETC.

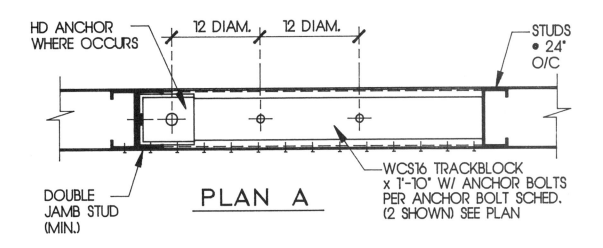

HD ANCHOR
WHERE OCCURS

12 DIAM.  12 DIAM.

STUDS
● 24"
O/C

DOUBLE
JAMB STUD
(MIN.)

## PLAN A

WCS16 TRACKBLOCK
x 1'-10" W/ ANCHOR BOLTS
PER ANCHOR BOLT SCHED.
(2 SHOWN) SEE PLAN

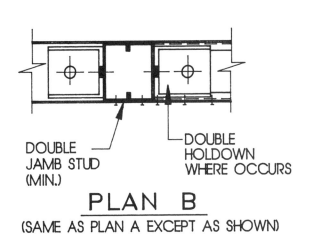

DOUBLE
JAMB STUD
(MIN.)

DOUBLE
HOLDOWN
WHERE OCCURS

## PLAN B
(SAME AS PLAN A EXCEPT AS SHOWN)

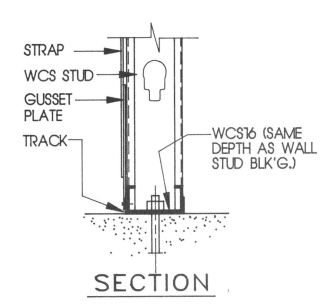

STRAP

WCS STUD

GUSSET
PLATE

TRACK

WCS16 (SAME
DEPTH AS WALL
STUD BLK'G.)

## SECTION

---

## SHEAR WALL TRACK REINFORCEMENT
## AND ANCHORAGE

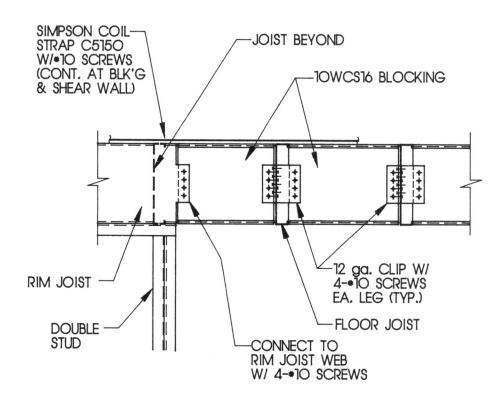

SIMPSON COIL-
STRAP C5150
W/#10 SCREWS
(CONT. AT BLK'G
& SHEAR WALL)

JOIST BEYOND

10WCS16 BLOCKING

12 ga. CLIP W/
4-#10 SCREWS
EA. LEG (TYP.)

FLOOR JOIST

RIM JOIST

DOUBLE
STUD

CONNECT TO
RIM JOIST WEB
W/ 4-#10 SCREWS

**F.26**   DRAG STRUT BLOCKING INTO FLOOR DIAPHRAGM

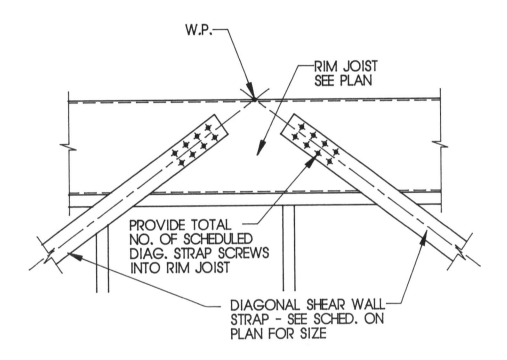

W.P.

RIM JOIST
SEE PLAN

PROVIDE TOTAL
NO. OF SCHEDULED
DIAG. STRAP SCREWS
INTO RIM JOIST

DIAGONAL SHEAR WALL
STRAP - SEE SCHED. ON
PLAN FOR SIZE

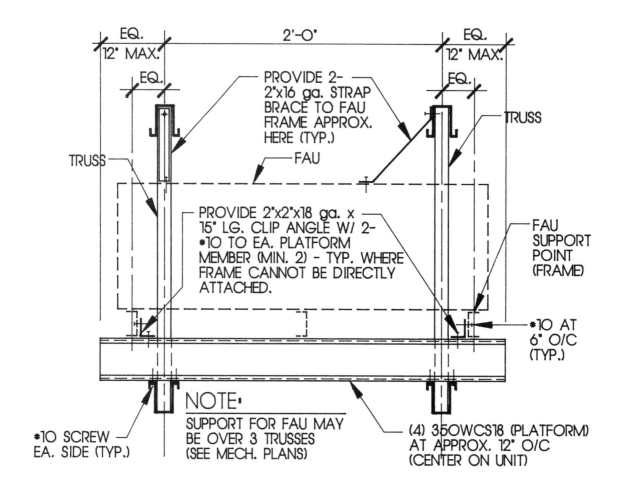

EQ.
12" MAX.

EQ.

2'-0"

EQ.
12" MAX.

EQ.

PROVIDE 2-
2"x16 ga. STRAP
BRACE TO FAU
FRAME APPROX.
HERE (TYP.)

TRUSS

TRUSS

FAU

PROVIDE 2"x2"x18 ga. x
15" LG. CLIP ANGLE W/ 2-
#10 TO EA. PLATFORM
MEMBER (MIN. 2) - TYP. WHERE
FRAME CANNOT BE DIRECTLY
ATTACHED.

FAU
SUPPORT
POINT
(FRAME)

#10 AT
6" O/C
(TYP.)

NOTE:
SUPPORT FOR FAU MAY
BE OVER 3 TRUSSES
(SEE MECH. PLANS)

#10 SCREW
EA. SIDE (TYP.)

(4) 350WCS18 (PLATFORM)
AT APPROX. 12" O/C
(CENTER ON UNIT)

**F.28**   **MECHANICAL UNIT SUPPORT BETWEEN
TRUSSES IN ATTIC SPACE**

## Comparative Framing Designs (Wood vs. Light-Gauge Steel)

1. Design Conditions:
   a. Framed area, spans, supports and bracing.
   b. Rafters supporting drywall ceiling.
   c. Roof system sloped at 4:12

2. Design Criteria:
   a. Live Load 20 lb/ft$^2$
   b. Dead Load: 18 lb./ft$^2$
   c. Limiting Deflection (live load only): 1/240 clear-span.

## Roof Framing Comparison

| Wood | Framing Item | Light-Gauge Steel |
|---|---|---|
| #2 kiln-dried Spruce-Pine-Fir 2x10 @ 16" O.C., notched to bear on ridge beam, 2x12 ridge board over beam, 16d common wire nails. | Rafter Size / Spacing / Span Condition | 6", 18 ga. rafter at 24" O.C. full-length, lapped at ridge over beam support, #10 Tek screws. |
| Rafter notched to bear on wall, toe-nailed with 8d common wire nails or attached by manufactured hurricane ties. | Exterior Wall Attachment | Connection clip with $^3/_4$" #10 Tek Screws. |
| 2x10 sub-fascia, 16d common wire nails; 1x12 fascia, 8d common wire nails. | Rafter End Closure | 6", 18 ga. Rim Track with $^3/_4$" #10 Low Profile Pan Head Screws to Web Stiffener and from Web Stiffener to rafter, 1x8 Wood Fascia to Rim Track with 1 $^1/_8$" screw-shank nails. |
| 8d common wire nails, toe-nailed. | Rafter to Ridge Beam Attachment | Connection clips, $^1/_2$" #10 Tek Pan Head screws. |
| $^1/_2$" CDX plywood, 8d common wire nails. | Roof Sheathing, and Attachment to Rafters | $^1/_2$" CDX plywood, 1" #10 Plyteks with Pilot Point. |

The above data has been provided for comparative purposes only and must *not* be used for design. Consult manufacturers' data for design values and specifications.

# G. FASTENING SCHEDULE RECOMMENDATIONS

## Recommended Fasteners in Floor Framing

| Materials | Fastener | Frequency or Quantity |
|---|---|---|
| Joist to Wood Sill | 1" #10 Teks Pancake Head | 1 @ each Joist to Wood Sill |
| Joist to Girder | $1/2$" #10 Teks Pan Head | 1 @ Joist to Girder |
| Joist to Connection Clip | $1/2$" #10 Teks Pan Head | 3 to 4 @ each clip |
| Bridging to Joist | $1/2$" #10 Teks Pan Head | 1 @ each joist |
| Joist to 2x Wood End Stiffener | 1 $1/4$" #10 Teks Pancake Head | 1 @ each Joist Web to Stiffener |
| End Stiffener to Joist | $3/4$" #10 Teks Pan Head | 3 to 4 @ each Stiffener to Joist |
| End Stiffener to Wood Rim Joist | 8d Common Wire Nail | 2 @ each End Stiffener to Rim Joist |
| Steel Rim Joist to End Stiffener | $3/4$" #10 Teks Pan Head | 3 @ each Joist |
| Steel Rim Track to End Stiffener | $3/4$" #10 Teks Pan Head | 3 @ each Joist |
| Joist Hanger to Joist | $7/8$" #10 Teks Pan Head | 3 @ each Joist |
| Joist to Overlapping Joist | $3/4$" #10 Teks Pan Head | 3 @ Support |
| Wood Sole Plate (Wall) to Rim Joist & Track | 2 $1/2$" #12 Teks Flat Head | 1 @ 24" O.C. & Max. 12" from each end of Track |
| Plate Track (Bottom) to Joist & Track | 1 $15/16$" #12 Teks Pan Head with Pilot Point | 1 @ 24" O.C. & Max. 12" from each end of Track |

Notes:
    (1)  Low Profile Pan Head is used in lieu of Pan Head where least projection of fastener is desired.
    (2)  S-7 point will substitute S-12 when attaching .07" members together.
    (3)  Teks/2 will be substituted by Teks/3 when steel thickness varies between .09" to .250".

The above data has been provided for comparative purposes only and must *not* be used for design. Consult manufacturers' data for design values and specifications.

# G. FASTENING SCHEDULE RECOMMENDATIONS

**Recommended Fasteners in Wall framing (Load Bearing)**

| Materials | Fastener | Frequency or Quantity |
|---|---|---|
| Stud to Plate Track (Bottom) | $3/4$" #8 Teks Low Profile Pan Head | 1 @ each Flange |
| Stud to Plate Track (Top) | $3/4$" #8 Teks Low Profile Pan Head | 1 @ each Flange |
| Diagonal Bracing to Stud | $1/2$" #8 Teks Low Profile Pan Head | 1 @ each Stud |
| Lateral Bracing to Stud | $3/4$" #8 Teks Pan Head | 1 @ each Stud Per Strap or 3 @ each connection clip with Cold Rolled Channel |
| Gusset to Stud | $3/4$" #10 Teks Low Profile Pan Head | Quantity and Spacing as per Loading |
| Stud to Stud (Nested) | $3/4$" #8 Teks Pan Head | 1 @ 24" O.C. through Flange |
| Stud to Stud (Back to Back) | $3/4$" #8 Teks Pan Head | 1 @ 24" O.C. through Web |
| Stud to Stud (@ Wall Intersection) | $3/4$" #10 Teks Pan Head | 1 @ 24" O.C. or 1 @ each Blocking |
| Lintel to Stud | $3/4$" #10 Teks Pan Head | Requirement Varies with Different Loading |

Notes:
  (1) Low Profile Pan Head is used in lieu of Pan Head where least projection of fastener is desired.
  (2) S-7 point will substitute S-12 when attaching .07" members together.
  (3) Teks/2 will be substituted by Teks/3 when steel thickness varies between .09" to .250".

The above data has been provided for comparative purposes only and must *not* be used for design. Consult manufacturers' data for design values and specifications.

## WALL FRAMING (LOAD BEARING)

# G. FASTENING SCHEDULE RECOMMENDATIONS

## Recommended Fasteners in Wall Framing (Non-Load-Bearing / Drywall)

| Materials | Fastener | Frequency or Quantity |
| --- | --- | --- |
| Stud to Plate Track (Bottom) | $1/2$" #8 Tek Screws Low Profile Pan Head | 1 @ each Flange |
| Stud to Plate Track (Top) | $1/2$" #8 Tek Screws Low Profile Pan Head | 1 @ each Flange |
| Lateral Bracing to Stud | $1/2$" #8 Tek Screws Pan Head | 2 @ Flange |
| Stud to Stud (Nested) | $1/2$" #10 Tek Screws Pan Head | 1 @ 24" O.C. |
| Stud to Stud (Back to Back) | $1/2$" #10 Tek Screws Pan Head | 1 @ 24" O.C. |
| Stud to Stud (@ Wall Intersection) | $1/2$" #10 Tek Screws Pan Head | 1 @ 24" O.C. or 1 @ each Blocking |

Notes:
  (1)  Low Profile Pan Head is used in lieu of Pan Head where least projection of fastener is desired.
  (2)  S-7 point will substitute S-12 when attaching .07" members together.
  (3)  Teks/2 will be substituted by Teks/3 when steel thickness varies between .09" to .250".

The above data has been provided for comparative purposes only and must *not* be used for design. Consult manufacturers' data for design values and specifications.

# G. FASTENING SCHEDULE RECOMMENDATIONS

**Recommended Fasteners in Roof Framing**

| Materials | Fastener | Frequency or Quantity |
|---|---|---|
| Ceiling Joist to Wood Top Plate | 1" #12 Teks Pan Head | 1 @ each Joist |
| Ceiling Joist to Top Plate Track | 3/4" #10 Teks Pan Head | 1 @ each Joist |
| Connection Clip to Wood Top Plate | 1" #12 Teks Pancake Head | 4 @ each Clip to Top Plate |
| Connection Clip to Top Plate Track | 3/4" #10 Teks Pan Head | 4 @ each Clip to Plate Track |
| Connection Clip to Ceiling Joist | 3/4" #10 Teks Pan Head | Min. 3 @ each Clip to Ceiling Joist and as per Loading |
| Connection Clip to Rafter | 3/4" #10 Teks Pan Head | Min. 3 @ each Clip to Rafter and as per Loading |
| Ceiling Joist to Parallel Rafter | 3/4" #10 Teks Pan Head | No. varies as per Loading |
| Ceiling Joist to Truss Web | 3/4" #10 Teks Pan Head | Min. 2 @ Flange and as per Loading |
| Ceiling Joist, Overlapped at Support | 3/4" #10 Teks Pan Head | Min. 2 @ Web |
| Connection Clip to Ridge Board | 3/4" #10 Teks Pan Head | 4 – 6 @ each Clip to Ridge |
| Rafters Overlapped at Ridge | 3/4" #10 Teks Pan Head | Min. 6 @ Overlapped Web Section and as per Loading |
| Built up Beam (Ridge Board) | 3/4" #10 Teks Pan Head | 1 @ each Flange @ 12" O.C. |
| Stiffback Bracing to Joist | 3/4" #10 Teks Pan Head | Min. 2 @ each Joist |
| Sub-Fascia Track to Rafter | 3/4" #10 Teks Low Profile Pan Head | 1 @ each Connection Clip and Max Top Plate |
| Wood Fascia to Sub-Fascia Track | 1 5/8" #12 Teks Trim Head | 2 @ 24" O.C. and @ maximum of 12" from Each End of Board or Corner |

Notes:
(1) Low Profile Pan Head is used in lieu of Pan Head where least projection of fastener is desired.
(2) S-7 point will substitute S-12 when attaching .07" members together.
(3) Teks/2 will be substituted by Teks/3 when steel thickness varies between .09" to .250".
(4) Where wood is fastened to steel channels, common wire nails and screw shank nails can be used in place of screws.

The above data has been provided for comparative purposes only and must *not* be used for design. Consult manufacturers' data for design values and specifications.

# G. FASTENING SCHEDULE RECOMMENDATIONS

## Recommended Fasteners in Application of Single Ply Gypsum Wall Board

| Thickness of Gypsum Wallboard | Plane of Framing Surface | Long Dimension Gypsum Board in Relation to Direction of Framing Member | Max. Spacing of Framing Member | Screw Type & Size | Screw Edge | Screw Field | Screw Shank Nail Type & Size | without Adhesive Edge | without Adhesive Field | with Adhesive Edge | with Adhesive Field |
|---|---|---|---|---|---|---|---|---|---|---|---|
| $3/8" - 1/2"$ | Horizontal | Either Direction | 16 | $7/8"$ Plytek | 6 | 12 | $1\,1/8"$ Screw Shank Nail | 6 | 8 | 16 | 16 |
| | Horizontal | Perpendicular | 24 | | 6 | 12 | | 6 | 8 | 16 | 16 |
| | Vertical | Either Direction | 24 | | 6 | 12 | | 8 | 8 | 16 | 16 |
| $5/8" - 3/4"$ | Horizontal | Either Direction | 16 | $1\,1/8"$ Plytek | 6 | 12 | $1\,5/8"$ Screw Shank Nail | 6 | 8 | 16 | 16 |
| | Horizontal | Perpendicular | 24 | | 6 | 12 | | 6 | 8 | 16 | 16 |
| | Vertical | Either Direction | 24 | | 6 | 12 | | 8 | 8 | 16 | 16 |

The above data has been provided for comparative purposes only and must *not* be used for design. Consult manufacturers' data for design values and specifications.

# G. FASTENING SCHEDULE RECOMMENDATIONS

**Recommended Fasteners in Application of Single Ply Plywood for Combination Subfloor — Underlayment to Framing**

| Thickness of Plywood Wallboard | Plane of Framing Surface | Long Dimension Plywood Board in Relation to Direction of Framing Member | Max. Spacing of Framing Member | Screw Type & Size | Edge | Field | Screw Shank Nail Type & Size | without Adhesive Edge | without Adhesive Field | with Adhesive Edge | with Adhesive Field |
|---|---|---|---|---|---|---|---|---|---|---|---|
| 1/2" & Less | Horizontal | Either Direction | 16 | 1" #10 Plytek | 6 | 12 | 1 1/8" Screw Shank Nail | 6 | 12 | 6 | 12 |
| | Horizontal | Perpendicular | 24 | | 6 | 12 | | 6 | 12 | 6 | 12 |
| | Vertical | Either Direction | 24 | | 6 | 12 | | 6 | 12 | 6 | 12 |
| 5/8" & 3/4" | Horizontal | Either Direction | 16 | 1 1/8" #10 Plytek | 6 | 12 | 1 5/8" Screw Shank Nail | 6 | 12 | 6 | 12 |
| | Horizontal | Perpendicular | 24 | | 6 | 12 | | 6 | 12 | 6 | 12 |
| | Vertical | Either Direction | 24 | | 6 | 12 | | 6 | 12 | 6 | 12 |
| 7/8" – 1" | Horizontal | Either Direction | 16 | 1 5/8" #12 Plytek | 6 | 12 | 1 7/8" Screw Shank Nail | 6 | 12 | 6 | 12 |
| | Horizontal | Perpendicular | 24 | | 6 | 12 | | 6 | 12 | 6 | 12 |
| | Vertical | Either Direction | 24 | | 6 | 12 | | 6 | 12 | 6 | 12 |
| 1 1/8" – 1 1/4" | Horizontal | Either Direction | 16 | 2" #12 Plytek | 6 | 12 | 2 1/4" Screw Shank Nail | 6 | 12 | 6 | 12 |
| | Horizontal | Perpendicular | 24 | | 6 | 12 | | 6 | 12 | 6 | 12 |
| | Vertical | Either Direction | 24 | | 6 | 12 | | 6 | 12 | 6 | 12 |

NOTE: If nails are used in lieu of screws, use of adhesive is strongly recommended.

*The above data has been provided for comparative purposes only and must not be used for design. Consult manufacturers' data for design values and specifications.*

# G. FASTENING SCHEDULE RECOMMENDATIONS

**Recommended Fasteners in Application of Single Ply Plywood for Combination Subfloor— Underlayment to Framing**

| Thickness of Gypsum Plywood Subfloor | Plane of Framing Surface | Long Dimension Plywood Subfloor in Relation to Direction of Framing Member | Max. Spacing of Framing Member | Maximum Spacing of Fasteners | | | | | | | | |
|---|---|---|---|---|---|---|---|---|---|---|---|---|
| | | | | Screw | | | Screw Shank Nail | | | | | |
| | | | | Type & Size | Edge | Field | Type & Size | without Adhesive | | with Adhesive | | |
| | | | | | | | | Edge | Field | Edge | Field |
| ½" & Less | Horizontal | Either Direction | 16 | 1" Plytek | 6 | 12 | 1 ⅛" Screw Shank Nail | 6 | 12 | 6 | 12 |
| | Horizontal | Perpendicular | 24 | | 6 | 12 | | 6 | 12 | 6 | 12 |
| | Vertical | Either Direction | 24 | | 6 | 12 | | 6 | 12 | 6 | 12 |
| ⅝" & ¾" | Horizontal | Either Direction | 16 | 1 ⅛" Plytek | 6 | 12 | 1 ⅝"–2" Screw Shank Nail | 6 | 12 | 6 | 12 |
| | Horizontal | Perpendicular | 24 | | 6 | 12 | | 6 | 12 | 6 | 12 |
| | Vertical | Either Direction | 24 | | 6 | 12 | | 6 | 12 | 6 | 12 |
| ⅞" – 1" | Horizontal | Either Direction | 16 | 1 ⅝" Plytek | 6 | 12 | 1 ⅞" Screw Shank Nail | 6 | 12 | 6 | 12 |
| | Horizontal | Perpendicular | 24 | | 6 | 12 | | 6 | 12 | 6 | 12 |
| | Vertical | Either Direction | 24 | | 6 | 12 | | 6 | 12 | 6 | 12 |
| 1 ⅛" –1 ¼" | Horizontal | Either Direction | 16 | 2" Plytek | 6 | 12 | 2 ¼" Screw Shank Nail | 6 | 12 | 6 | 12 |
| | Horizontal | Perpendicular | 24 | | 6 | 12 | | 6 | 12 | 6 | 12 |
| | Vertical | Either Direction | 24 | | 6 | 12 | | 6 | 12 | 6 | 12 |

NOTE: If nails are used in lieu of screws, use of adhesive is strongly recommended.

The above data has been provided for comparative purposes only and must *not* be used for design. Consult manufacturers' data for design values and specifications.

# H. FASTENERS

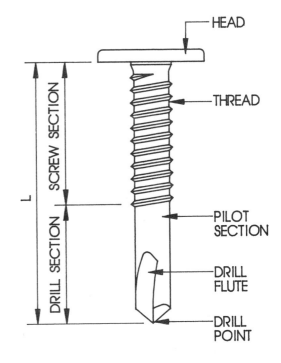

## Applications

| | | | |
|---|---|---|---|
| Floor Systems | A. Metal Lath to Joist<br>B. Joist to Wood Web<br>    Stiffener | C. Joist to Wood End<br>    Stiffener<br>D. Joist to Wood Sill | |
| Wall Systems | A. Metal Lath to Stud | B. Stud to Wood Web<br>    Stiffener | |
| Roof Systems | A. Metal Lath to Rafter<br>B. Rafter to Wood Web<br>    Stiffener | C. Ceiling Joist to Wood<br>    End Stiffener | |

*CHECK WITH MANUFACTURER FOR STANDARD AVAILABLE SIZES.*

## PANCAKE HEAD SCREW                                 H.1

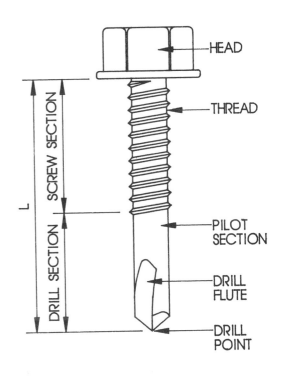

## Applications

| | | |
|---|---|---|
| Floor Systems | A. End Stiffener to Rim<br>B. Connection Clip to Joist<br>C. Joist to Web Stiffener<br>D. Bridging to Joist | E. Solid Blocking to Joist<br>F. Built-up Beam Assembly<br>G. Joist Hanger to Joist<br>H. Joist to Overlapping Joist |
| Wall System | A. Stud to Plate Track<br>B. Ladder-Back to Stud<br>C. Stud to Stud<br>D. Windbrace to Stud | E. Lateral Bracing to Stud<br>F. Gusset to Stud & Header<br>G. Window Sill to Stud<br>H. Lintel Assembly |
| Roof System | A. Subfascia to Rafter<br>B. Rafter to Rafter<br>C. Collar Tie to Rafter<br>D. Bridging to Rafter<br>E. Rafter to Ceiling Joist | F. Gusset to Rafter<br>G. King Post to Rafter<br>H. Truss Web to Rafter<br>I. Bracing to Rafter<br>J. Rafter to Web Stiffener |

*CHECK WITH MANUFACTURER FOR STANDARD AVAILABLE SIZES.*

## HEX WASHER HEAD SCREW                              H.2

# H. FASTENERS

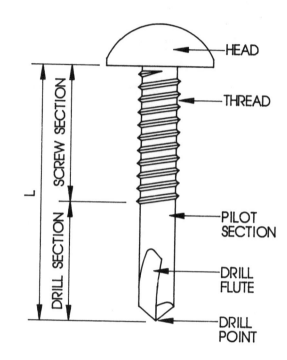

## Applications

| Floor Systems | | |
|---|---|---|
| A. End Stiffener to Rim | E. Solid Blocking to Joist | |
| B. Connection Clip to Joist | F. Built-up Beam Assembly | |
| C. Joist to Web Stiffener | G. Joist Hanger to Joist | |
| D. Bridging to Joist | H. Joist to Overlapping Joist | |

| Wall System | | |
|---|---|---|
| A. Stud to Plate Track | E. Lateral Bracing to Stud | |
| B. Ladder-Back to Stud | F. Gusset to Stud & Header | |
| C. Stud to Stud | G. Window Sill to Stud | |
| D. Windbrace to Stud | H. Lintel Assembly | |

| Roof System | | |
|---|---|---|
| A. Subfascia to Rafter | F. Gusset to Rafter | |
| B. Rafter to Rafter | G. King Post to Rafter | |
| C. Collar Tie to Rafter | H. Truss Web to Rafter | |
| D. Bridging to Rafter | I. Bracing to Rafter | |
| E. Rafter to Ceiling Joist | J. Rafter to Web Stiffener | |

*CHECK WITH MANUFACTURER FOR STANDARD AVAILABLE SIZES.*

HEAD
THREAD
PILOT SECTION
DRILL FLUTE
DRILL POINT
SCREW SECTION
DRILL SECTION
L

---

## H.3      PAN HEAD SCREW

## Applications

| Floor Systems | | |
|---|---|---|
| A. Joist to Rim Track | E. Solid Blocking to Joist | |
| B. Joist to Web Stiffener | F. Built-up Beam Assembly | |
| C. Connection Clip to Joist | G. Joist Hanger to Joist | |
| D. Bridging to Joist | H. Joist to Overlapping Joist | |

| Wall System | | |
|---|---|---|
| A. Stud to Plate Track | F. Gusset to Stud & Header | |
| B. Ladder-Back to Stud | G. Window Sill to Stud | |
| C. Stud to Stud | H. Lintel Assembly | |
| D. Windbrace to Stud | I. Steel Jamb to Stud | |
| E. Lateral Bracing to Stud | | |

| Roof System | | |
|---|---|---|
| A. Subfascia to Rafter | E. Gusset to Rafter | |
| B. Rafter to Rafter | F. Rafter to Web Stiffener | |
| C. Bracing to Rafter | G. Ridge Board Assembly | |
| D. Bridging to Rafter | | |

*CHECK WITH MANUFACTURER FOR STANDARD AVAILABLE SIZES.*

HEAD
THREAD
PILOT SECTION
DRILL FLUTE
DRILL POINT
SCREW SECTION
DRILL SECTION
L

---

## H.4      LOW- PROFILE PAN HEAD SCREW

# H. FASTENERS

## Applications

| | |
|---|---|
| Floor Systems | A. Trim Moulding to Joist |
| Wall Systems | A. Wood Trim to Stud |
| Roof Systems | A. Trim Attachment |

*CHECK WITH MANUFACTURER FOR STANDARD AVAILABLE SIZES.*

HEAD

THREAD

PILOT SECTION

DRILL FLUTE

DRILL POINT

SCREW SECTION

DRILL SECTION

L

## TRIM HEAD SCREW

**H.5**

---

## Applications

| | |
|---|---|
| Floor Systems | A. Trim Moulding to Joist |
| Wall Systems | A. Wood Cabinet to Stud<br>B. Trim Moulding to Stud |
| Roof Systems | A. Trim Moulding to Rafter |

*CHECK WITH MANUFACTURER FOR STANDARD AVAILABLE SIZES.*

HEAD

THREAD

PILOT SECTION

DRILL FLUTE

DRILL POINT

SCREW SECTION

DRILL SECTION

L

## OVAL HEAD SCREW

**H.6**

# H. FASTENERS

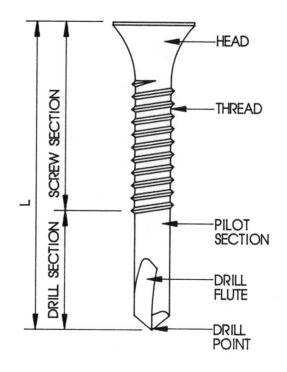

## Applications

| | | |
|---|---|---|
| Floor Systems | A. Joist to Wood Sill<br>B. Sheathing to Joist | C. Subflooring to Joist |
| Wall Systems | A. Drywall to Stud<br>B. Sheathing to Stud | C. Furring to Lath<br>D. Rigid Insulation to Stud |
| Roof Systems | A. Drywall to Rafter<br>B. Sheathing to Rafter | C. Drywall to Ceiling Joist<br>D. Rigid Insulation to Rafter |

*CHECK WITH MANUFACTURER FOR STANDARD AVAILABLE SIZES.*

**H.7**　　　　　　**BUGLE HEAD SCREW**

## Applications

| | | |
|---|---|---|
| Floor Systems | A. Sheathing to Joist | B. Subflooring to Joist |
| Wall Systems | A. Sheathing to Stud<br>B. Drywall to Stud | C. Ridge Insulation to Stud |
| Roof Systems | A. Sheathing to Rafter<br>B. Rigid Insulation to Rafter | C. Ruffing to Rafter<br>D. Drywall to Ceiling Joist |

*CHECK WITH MANUFACTURER FOR STANDARD AVAILABLE SIZES.*

**H.8**　　　　　　**SCREW-SHANK NAIL**

# H. FASTENERS

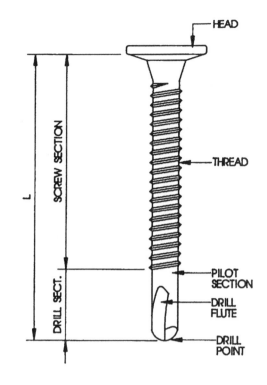

**HEAD**

**SCREW SECTION**

L

**THREAD**

**DRILL SECT.**

**PILOT SECTION**

**DRILL FLUTE**

**DRILL POINT**

| Applications | | |
|---|---|---|
| Floor Systems | A. | Wood Sheathing to Joists |
| Wall Systems | A. | Wood Sheathing to Studs and Track |
| Roof Systems | A. | Wood Sheathing to Trusses |
| | B. | Wood Sheathing to Joists / Rafters |

*CHECK WITH MANUFACTURER FOR STANDARD AVAILABLE SIZES.*

## PLY-TEK SCREW                    **H.9**

**HEAD**

**SCREW SECTION**

L

**THREAD**

**DRILL SECTION**

**PILOT SECTION**

**DRILL FLUTE**

**DRILL POINT**

| Applications | | |
|---|---|---|
| Floor Systems | A. | Floor Joists to Steel Beam |
| | B. | Angle Clips or Angles to Steel Beam |
| | C. | Joist Hangers to Steel Beam |
| | D. | Rim Track to Steel Beam |

*CHECK WITH MANUFACTURER FOR STANDARD AVAILABLE SIZES.*

## HEX HEAD SELF-DRILLING #5 SCREW        **H.10**

# MAS MUDSILL ANCHOR

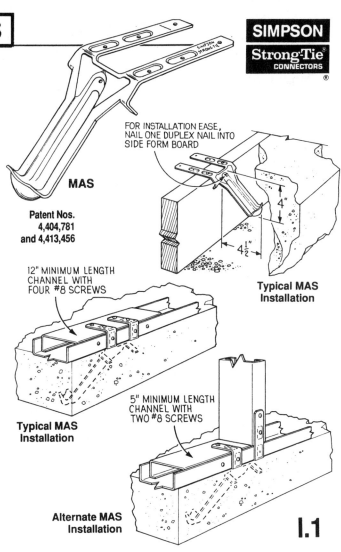

**MAS**

**Patent Nos.
4,404,781
and 4,413,456**

A fast, low installed cost mudsill anchor.

Fast for the finisher—Install before pouring concrete by nailing into form, or insert into concrete after pour. Finish up to edge of slab — no anchor bolts to hand-trowel around, no nuts or washers to lose. For slab or stemwall construction.

**MATERIAL:** 16 gauge

**FINISH:** Galvanized. Selected products available with Z-MAX coating; see Corrosion-Resistant Connectors.

**INSTALLATION:** ▪ Use all specified fasteners. See Screws, page 4.

- ▪ Not for use where (a) a horizontal cold joint exists between the slab and foundation wall or footing beneath, unless provisions are made to transfer the load, or (b) anchors are installed in slabs poured over foundation walls formed of concrete block.
- ▪ Use a minimum of 2 MAS anchors per track with one MAS located within 1′ from each end of each track.
- ▪ Channel section must be attached to the inside of the track for correct MAS installation.

FOR INSTALLATION EASE, NAIL ONE DUPLEX NAIL INTO SIDE FORM BOARD

**Typical MAS Installation**

12" MINIMUM LENGTH CHANNEL WITH FOUR #8 SCREWS

5" MINIMUM LENGTH CHANNEL WITH TWO #8 SCREWS

**Typical MAS Installation**

**Alternate MAS Installation**

| MODEL NO. | FASTENERS | | UPLIFT AVG ULT | ALLOWABLE LOADS (133) | | |
|---|---|---|---|---|---|---|
| | SIDES TOTAL | TOP | | UPLIFT | PARALLEL TO PLATE | PERP TO PLATE |
| MAS | 2- #10 | 4- #10 | 2108 | 845 | 975 | 290 |

1. Loads may not be increased for short-term loading.
2. For alternate installation, uplift load is 585 lbs, parallel-to-plate load is 580 lbs and perpendicular-to-plate is 220 lbs.

**I.1**

# MKP™ MONKEY PAW™ ANCHOR BOLT HOLDER

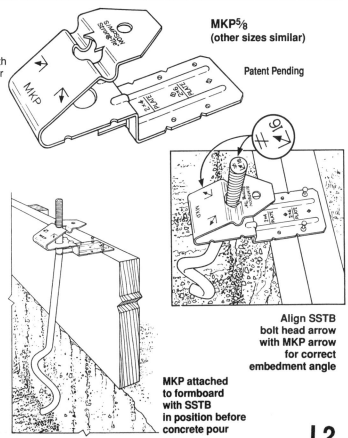

**MKP⅝**
**(other sizes similar)**

**Patent Pending**

New! Secure the SSTB to the formboard before the concrete pour with a MKP Monkey Paw Bolt Holder. The MKP offers significant savings over plywood or 2x wood holders. Available in ½", ⅝" and ¾" sizes.

**SPECIAL FEATURES:** ▪ The MKP may be used several times.

- ▪ Stabilizes bolt by providing three-point support against lateral concrete pressure.
- ▪ Alignment arrows (left or right) match the SSTB bolt head arrow.
- ▪ Stamped for 2x4 or 2x6 mudsill placement.
- ▪ No nut required to hold bolt in place.
- ▪ When removed, the MKP cleans the concrete from the bolt thread.

**MATERIAL:** 16 gauge

**FINISH:** Galvanized

**INSTALLATION:** ▪ Attach SSTB to the MKP. Line up MKP arrows with SSTB bolt head arrows for diagonal installation at approximately 45° from the wall.

- ▪ Align bottom tab of MKP with SSTB embedment line.
- ▪ Use 2x4 or 2x6 notches to match the mudsill size.
- ▪ Attach the MKP to the formboard using duplex nails.
- ▪ After concrete pour, allow concrete to cure. Remove the MKP by squeezing the top and bottom together, lifting and twisting off.

**Align SSTB bolt head arrow with MKP arrow for correct embedment angle**

**MKP attached to formboard with SSTB in position before concrete pour**

**I.2**

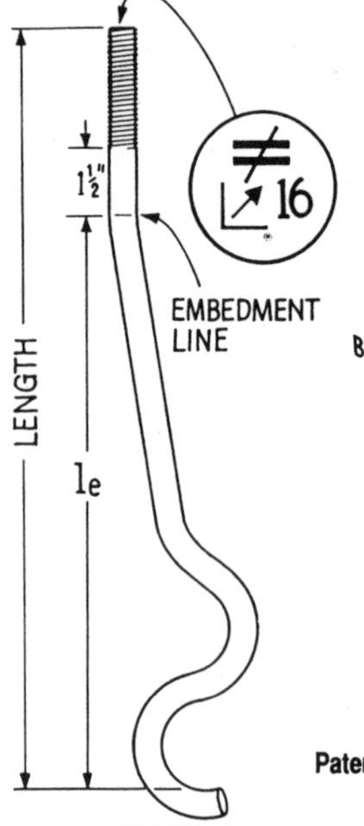

**SIMPSON**
**Strong-Tie® CONNECTORS ®**

# SSTB® ANCHOR BOLT

**Identification stamp showing embedment angle**

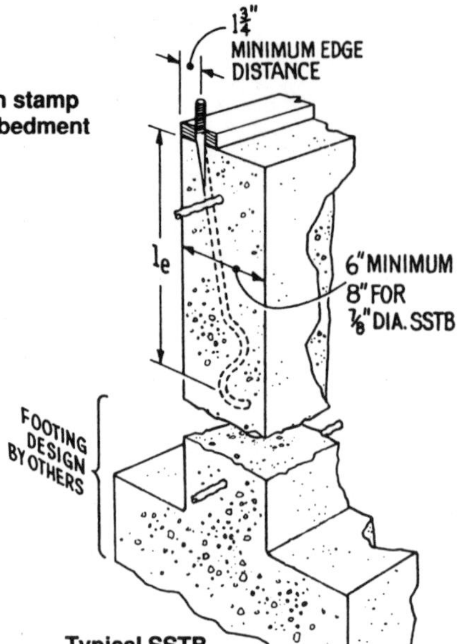

1¾" MINIMUM EDGE DISTANCE

1½"

≠ 16

EMBEDMENT LINE

LENGTH

l$_e$

6" MINIMUM 8" FOR ⅞" DIA. SSTB

l$_e$

FOOTING DESIGN BY OTHERS

**Typical SSTB Installation**

**SSTB16 (others similar)**

**Patent Pending**

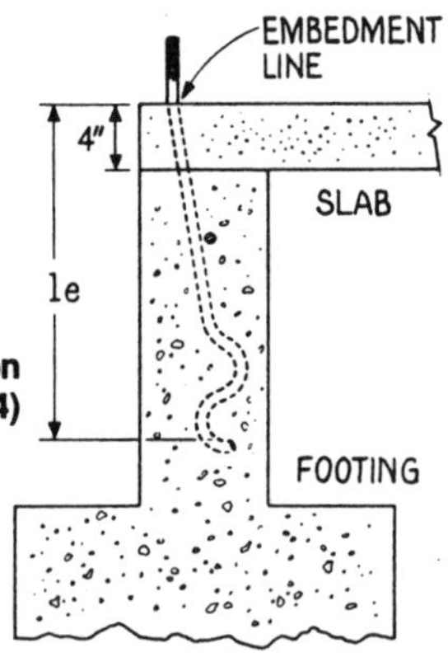

**Double Pour Installation (SSTB20, 24 and 34)**

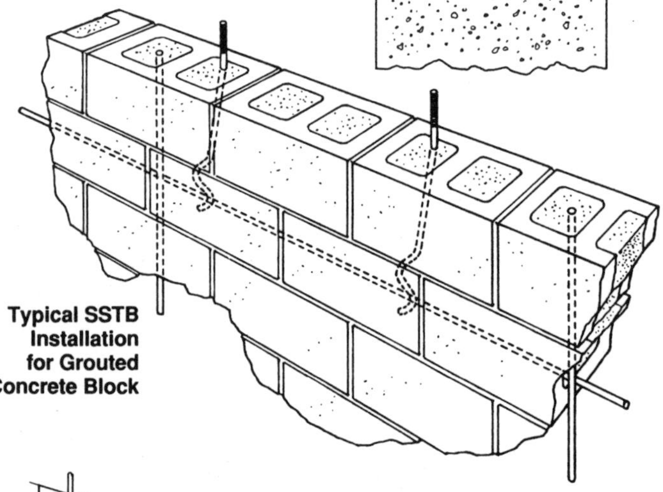

EMBEDMENT LINE

4"

SLAB

l$_e$

FOOTING

**Typical SSTB Installation for Grouted Concrete Block**

The SSTB Anchor Bolt is the first tested and inspection-friendly anchor bolt for Holdowns.

Previously called the STAB, the name was changed to eliminate misinstallation by stabbing the bolt into wet concrete. Extensive testing has been done on the SSTB to determine the design load capacity at a common application, the garage stem wall. The design loads are based on the lowest ultimate, from a series of five tests, with a three times safety factor.

**SPECIAL FEATURES:** ■ Rolled threads for higher tensile capacity.
- Offset angle to reduce side-bursting and provide more concrete cover.
- Stamped bolt head for identification after pour.
- Stamped embedment line to aid installation.
- Configuration results in minimum rebar interference.

**INSTALLATION:** ■ Use the table to select the appropriate SSTB. SSTB is suitable for monolithic and two pour installations.
- Nuts and washers are not supplied with the SSTB; install standard nuts, couplers and/or washers as required.

**CONCRETE FOUNDATION**
- Install SSTB before the concrete pour using an MKP. Install the SSTB diagonally at approximately 45° from the wall. Install one #4 rebar 3" to 5" from the top of the foundation.
- Minimum concrete compression strength is 2500 psi. Unless noted otherwise, no special inspection is required for foundation concrete when the structural design is based on concrete no greater than 2500 psi (1991 UBC, section 306 (a)1).
- Use 90% of the table load for 2000 psi concrete.

**REINFORCED CONCRETE BLOCK**
- Install before concrete pour diagonally at approximately 45° in the cell.
- Install one #4 horizontal rebar approx. 12" from the top and #4 vertical rebar minimum 48" o.c.
- Grout all cells with minimum 2000 psi concrete.

**OPTIONS**: Other SSTB sizes available; contact Simpson for details.
**CODE NUMBERS**: ICBO No. 4935 and City of L.A. No. RR 25152 for concrete foundation only.

### SSTB SELECTION TABLE

| MODEL NO. | MONO POUR | TWO POUR |
|---|---|---|
| S/HD8 | SSTB28 | SSTB34 |
| S/HD10 | SSTB28 | SSTB34 |

| MODEL NO. | DIA | L | MIN EMBED l$_e$ | CONCRETE [4,5] EARTHQUAKE | WIND | CONCRETE BLOCK [3] EARTHQUAKE | WIND |
|---|---|---|---|---|---|---|---|
| SSTB16 | ⅝ | 17 | 12 | 4420 | 3890 | 4630 | 4085 |
| SSTB20 | ⅝ | 21 | 16 | 4600 | 4050 | 4630 | 4085 |
| SSTB24 | ⅝ | 25 | 20 | 4600 | 4050 | 4630 | 4085 |
| SSTB28 | ⅞ | 29 | 24 | 10100 | 8890 | — | — |
| SSTB34 | ⅞ | 34 | 28 | 10100 | 8890 | — | — |
| SSTB36 | ⅞ | 36 | 28 | 10100 | 8890 | — | — |

*(Header: MAXIMUM ALLOWABLE TENSION LOAD (133))*

1. Loads may not be increased for short-term loading. Loads apply to wind and earthquake loading per UBC Section 2624 and 2625.
2. Minimum anchor center-to-center spacing is 2l$_e$ for anchors acting in tension at the same time for the full load.
3. SSTB with ⅞" dia. have not been tested yet.
4. The maximum allowable load is 8150 lbs. for a SSTB28 used 5" from the end of a concrete foundation. Use the full table load when installed 24" from the end or when installed in the corner condition (see illustration).
5. The SSTB was tested in a stem wall with a minimum amount of concrete cover.

**TYPICAL REBAR PLACEMENT**

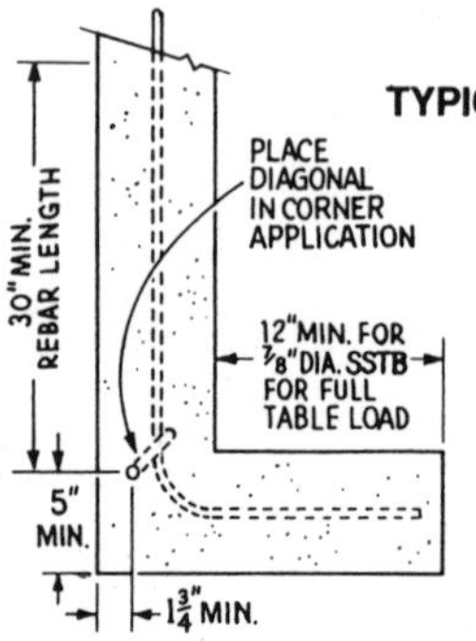

30" MIN. REBAR LENGTH

PLACE DIAGONAL IN CORNER APPLICATION

12" MIN. FOR ⅞" DIA. SSTB FOR FULL TABLE LOAD

5" MIN.

1¾" MIN.

**Corner Installation**

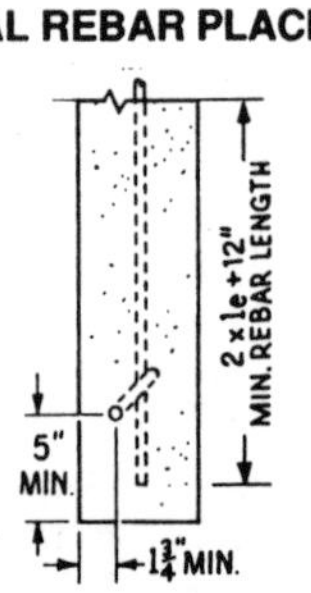

2 x l$_e$ +12" MIN. REBAR LENGTH

5" MIN.

1¾" MIN.

**End Wall Installation**

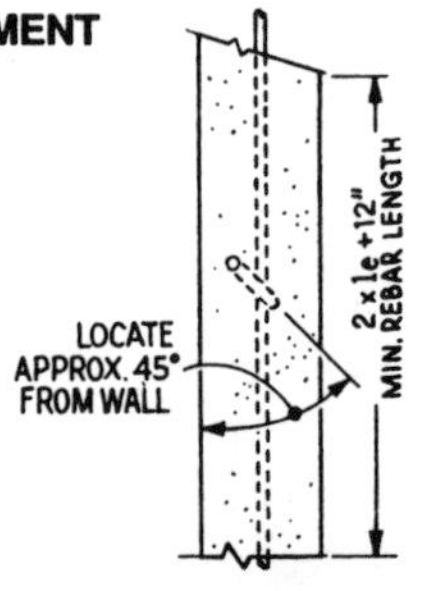

LOCATE APPROX. 45° FROM WALL

2 x l$_e$ +12" MIN. REBAR LENGTH

**Continuous Stem Wall Installation**

**I.3**

# I. HARDWARE / CONNECTORS

## ET *EPOXY TIE™*

Epoxies offer stronger bonding, shorter cure time and less hydrolization than other types of resin anchors. Simpson's ET22 Epoxy-Tie is a two-component amine-based system for high strength anchoring, with a one year shelf life.

**Components and Features:**
- The ET system has a dual-cartridge, a disposable static mixing nozzle that blends the resin and hardener thoroughly, and a dispensing tool.
- The epoxy is dispensed directly into the anchoring hole, with no waste or mess. ET's unique transparent measuring gauge on the cartridge allows the exact amount to be dispensed.
- The ET is resistant to hydrolization, which occurs when the bond breaks down in the presence of water. The gel consistency allows the material to be injected horizontally as well as vertically.

**Installation (see drawings below) :**
1. Drill hole to specified diameter and depth.
2. Remove dust from hole with manual blower or compressed air. Clean with nylon brush. Dust left in hole will reduce the epoxy's holding capacity.
3. Dispense bead of ET to check for proper mixture, shown by a uniform gray color.
4. Fill hole halfway with ET, starting from the bottom of the hole to avoid air pockets. Withdraw mixing nozzle as the hole is being filled.
5. Insert anchor, turning slowly until the anchor hits the bottom of the hole.

**Codes:** ICBO # 4945. The ET meets the following specifications: ASTM C 881-90 Standard Specification for Epoxy-Resin-Base Bonding Systems for Concrete. ASTM E 488-90 Standard Test Methods for Strength of Anchors in Concrete and Masonry Elements.

### Set Schedule

| 40°F | 60°F | 80°F | 100°F |
|---|---|---|---|
| 18 hrs | 6 hrs | 4 hrs | 4 hrs |

Do not disturb anchors during set time.

### Cure Schedule

| 40°F | 60°F | 80°F | 100°F |
|---|---|---|---|
| 72 hrs | 24 hrs | 24 hrs | 12 hrs |

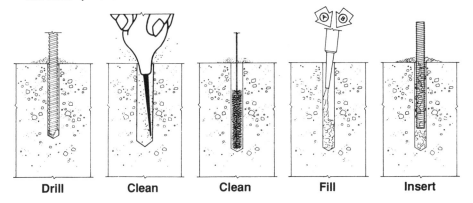

**Drill**    **Clean**    **Clean**    **Fill**    **Insert**

## ALLOWABLE LOADS FOR THREADED ROD

| STUD DIAMETER | DRILL BIT DIAMETER | MINIMUM EMBEDMENT DEPTH | SPACING (s) | EDGE DISTANCE (m) | ALLOWABLE TENSILE LOADS | | | | | ALLOWABLE SHEAR LOADS | | | | |
|---|---|---|---|---|---|---|---|---|---|---|---|---|---|---|
| | | | | | BASED ON BOND STRENGTH | | BASED ON STEEL STRENGTH | | | BASED ON BOND STRENGTH | | BASED ON STEEL STRENGTH | | |
| | | | | | fc = 2500 | fc = 4500 | A 307 (SAE 1018) | A 193 Gr. B (SAE 4140) | SS 304 | fc = 2500 | fc = 4500 | A 307 (SAE 1018) | A 193 Gr. B (SAE 4140) | SS 304 |
| 3/8" | 7/16" | 3 1/2" | 4 1/2" | 2 5/8" | 2220 | 2895 | 2080 | 4580 | 1670 | 1020 | 1020 | 1040 | 2290 | 1040 |
| 1/2" | 9/16" | 4 1/4" | 6" | 3 1/4" | 2595 | 4310 | 3730 | 8210 | 2990 | 2415 | 2415 | 1870 | 4110 | 1870 |
| 5/8" | 3/4" | 5" | 7 1/2" | 3 3/4" | 4375 | 6170 | 5870 | 12910 | 4700 | 3485 | 3485 | 2940 | 6460 | 2940 |
| 3/4" | 7/8" | 6 3/4" | 9" | 5" | 6970 | 7325 | 8490 | 18680 | 6790 | 6480 | 6480 | 4250 | 9340 | 4250 |
| 7/8" | 1" | 7 1/2" | 10 1/2" | 5 5/8" | 8005 | 10640 | 12000 | 26400 | 9500 | 6240 | 6720 | 6000 | 12800 | 6000 |
| 1" | 1 1/8" | 8 1/4" | 12" | 6 1/4" | 10450 | 12400 | 15700 | 34500 | 12500 | 7185 | 7200 | 7820 | 17200 | 7820 |

1. Allowable loads for bond strength are based on a factor of safety of four on the average ultimate load. They may not be increased for load duration. Allowable load must be the lesser of the bond or steel strength.

2. The tabulated values are for anchors installed at the specified spacing and edge distances. Spacing and edge distances may be reduced in accordance with the table below. Linear interpolation may be used for intermediate spacings.

3. The anchors experience a reduction in tensile and shear capacity with increased ambient temperatures. For reduction values for temperatures above 72°F, consult Simpson's S-ETC brochure.

| TENSION CAPACITY | | SHEAR CAPACITY | | |
|---|---|---|---|---|
| SPACING (s) AND EDGE DISTANCE (m) | FACTOR (Ft) | EDGE DISTANCE (m) | DIRECTION OF LOAD | FACTOR (Fs) |
| Spacing min = 0.5s | 0.5 | 0.5m | Toward edge | 0.5 |
| Edge distance min = 0.5m | 0.5 | 0.5m | Away from edge | 0.5 |

1. Linear interpolation is allowed for edge distances which fall between 0.5m and 1.0m, and anchor spacing which falls between 0.5s and 1.0s.

**I.4**

# S/PAHD, S/MPAHD, S/HPAHD HOLDOWNS

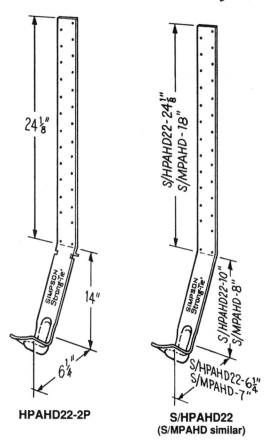

**HPAHD22-2P**

**S/HPAHD22**
**(S/MPAHD similar)**

A variety of steel-to-concrete connectors that satisfy engineering and code requirements. Allowable loads include a tested three-times safety factor in concrete. One-piece design; no separate anchors required.

**MATERIAL:** S/HPA and HPA—10 gauge x 2$\frac{1}{16}$"; all others—12 gauge x 2$\frac{1}{16}$"

**FINISH:** Galvanized. Selected products available in Z-MAX coating; see Corrosion-Resistant Connectors.

**INSTALLATION:** ■ Use all specified fasteners. See Screws, page 4.
- Unless otherwise noted, do NOT install where:
  (a) a horizontal cold joint exists within the embedment depth between the slab and foundation wall or footing beneath, unless provisions are made to transfer the load, or the slab is designed to resist the load imposed by the anchor; or
  (b) slabs are poured over concrete block foundation walls.
- To get the full table load, the minimum center-to-center spacing is twice the embedment depth when resisting tension loads at the same time.
- **FOUNDATION CORNERS:** Screw quantities have been reduced when the load is limited by tested concrete pullout strength. Additional screw holes need not be filled.
- Loads are calculated using a 4" slab over 8" and 10" foundation walls.

**S/PAHD42, S/MPAHD, S/HPAHD22, HPAHD22-2P HOLDOWNS:**
Designed to be installed at the edge of concrete. Tests determined the pullout strength with one horizontal #4 rebar in the shear cone.

Install before pouring concrete by nailing to the form. Pre-bent to control the embedment at the required angle; field-bending is not necessary.

Installation holes allow nailing to the form, resulting in 1" deeper embedment; see illustration.

**OPTIONS:** See also S/HD Holdowns, S/LTT and S/MTT Tension Ties.

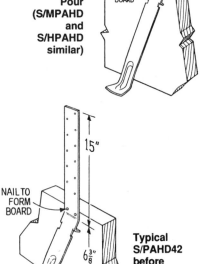

**Typical HPAHD22-2P before Concrete Pour (S/MPAHD and S/HPAHD similar)**

**Typical S/PAHD42 before Concrete Pour**

| MODEL NO. | MINIMUM FOOTING WIDTH | SCREWS | ALLOWABLE LOADS (133) |
|---|---|---|---|
| **EDGE INSTALLATION—2500 PSI CONCRETE** | | | |
| **SINGLE POUR—see installation 1–8" min from corner** | | | |
| S/PAHD42 | 6 | 7- #10 | 2205 |
| | 8 | 9- #10 | 2945 |
| S/MPAHD | 6 | 9- #10 | 2800 |
| | 8 | 12- #10 | 3665 |
| S/HPAHD22 | 6 | 10- #10 | 3150 |
| | 8 | 14- #10 | 4370 |
| **DOUBLE POUR—see installation 3–8" min from corner** | | | |
| S/PAHD42 | 6 | 7- #10 | 2205 |
| | 8 | 7- #10 | 2255 |
| S/MPAHD | 6 | 9- #10 | 2800 |
| | 8 | 12- #10 | 3665 |
| S/HPAHD22 | 6 | 10- #10 | 3150 |
| | 8 | 12- #10 | 3950 |
| HPAHD22-2P | 6 | 10- #10 | 3150 |
| | 8 | 14- #10 | 4415 |

| MODEL NO. | MINIMUM FOOTING WIDTH | SCREWS | ALLOWABLE LOADS (133) |
|---|---|---|---|
| **CORNER INSTALLATION—2000 PSI CONCRETE** | | | |
| **SINGLE POUR—see installation 2—½" min from corner** | | | |
| S/PAHD42 | 6 | 4- #10 | 1225 |
| | 8 | 5- #10 | 1400 |
| S/MPAHD | 6 | 4- #10 | 1135 |
| | 8 | 6- #10 | 1840 |
| S/HPAHD22 | 6 | 6- #10 | 1750 |
| | 8 | 7- #10 | 2210 |
| **DOUBLE POUR—see installation 4—½" min from corner** | | | |
| S/PAHD42 | 6 | 4- #10 | 1225 |
| | 8 | 5- #10 | 1400 |
| S/MPAHD | 6 | 4- #10 | 1135 |
| | 8 | 6- #10 | 1840 |
| S/HPAHD22 | 6 | 6- #10 | 1750 |
| | 8 | 7- #10 | 2210 |
| HPAHD22-2P | 6 | 7- #10 | 2210 |
| | 8 | 7- #10 | 2210 |

1. S/HPAHD22 may be embedded 4" into the slab and 6" into the 8" footing beneath for a maximum load of 2810 lbs. at 8" minimum from the closest corner, and 1400 lbs. at ½" from the closest corner.

2. EDGE INSTALLATION: The minimum concrete compression strength is 2500 psi. For 2000 psi, calculate loads at 0.75 of the table allowable loads.
CORNER INSTALLATION: The minimum concrete compression strength is 2000 psi. No load reduction is allowed.

3. Allowable loads have been increased 33% for wind or earthquake loading with no further increase allowed.

4. Calculate the loads using straight line interpolation for corner distances between ½" and 8".

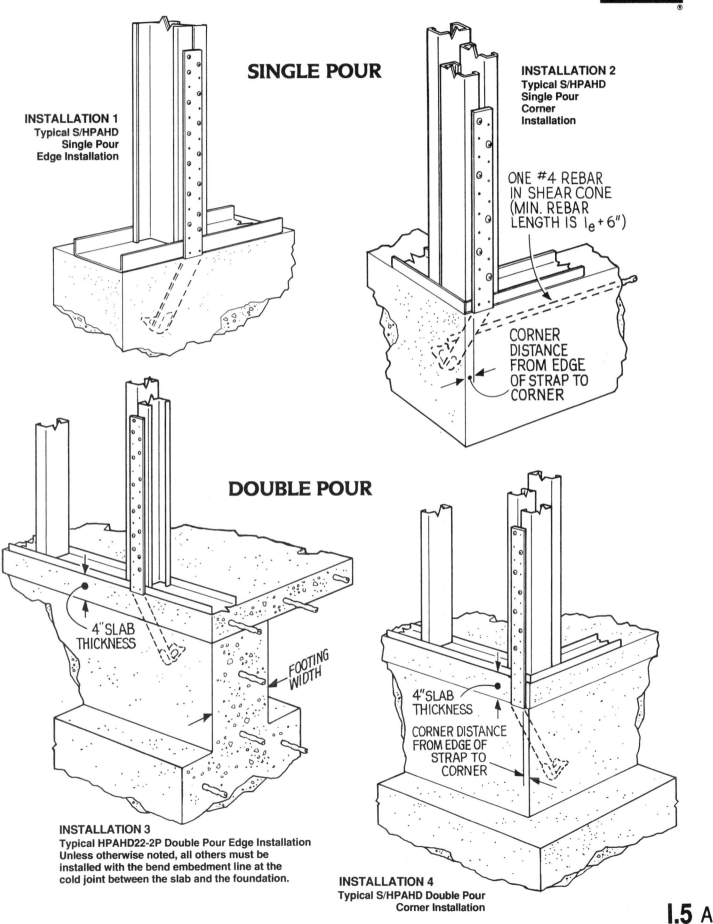

**SINGLE POUR**

**INSTALLATION 1**
**Typical S/HPAHD**
**Single Pour**
**Edge Installation**

**INSTALLATION 2**
**Typical S/HPAHD**
**Single Pour**
**Corner**
**Installation**

ONE #4 REBAR
IN SHEAR CONE
(MIN. REBAR
LENGTH IS $l_e + 6''$)

CORNER
DISTANCE
FROM EDGE
OF STRAP TO
CORNER

**DOUBLE POUR**

4" SLAB
THICKNESS

FOOTING
WIDTH

4" SLAB
THICKNESS

CORNER DISTANCE
FROM EDGE OF
STRAP TO
CORNER

**INSTALLATION 3**
**Typical HPAHD22-2P Double Pour Edge Installation**
**Unless otherwise noted, all others must be**
**installed with the bend embedment line at the**
**cold joint between the slab and the foundation.**

**INSTALLATION 4**
**Typical S/HPAHD Double Pour**
**Corner Installation**

**I.5** A

Details and drawings provided courtesy of Simpson Strong-Tie Company, Inc.

**SIMPSON**
**Strong-Tie®**
**CONNECTORS**

# S/HD HOLDOWNS

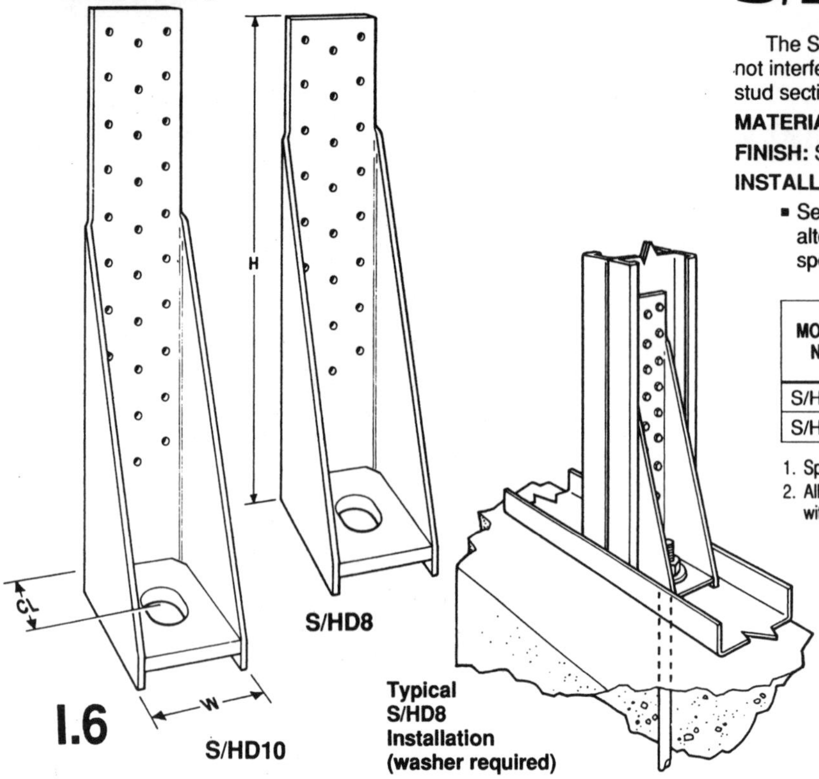

The S/HD's design makes installation easy. The connector height does not interfere with stud knockouts, and the narrow width fits within the stud section.

**MATERIAL:** S/HD8—10 ga with ¼" plate; S/HD10—10 ga with ⅜" plate

**FINISH:** Simpson gray paint

**INSTALLATION:** ▪ Use all specified fasteners. See Screws, page 4.
▪ See SSTB Anchor Bolts. The design engineer may specify any alternate anchorage calculated to resist the tension load for your specific job.

| MODEL NO. | DIMENSIONS | | | FASTENERS | | AVG ULT | ALLOWABLE LOAD |
|---|---|---|---|---|---|---|---|
| | W | H | CL | ANCHOR DIA | SCREWS | | |
| S/HD8 | 2½ | 13⅞ | 1½ | ⅞ | 24- #10 | 21167 | 7920 |
| S/HD10 | 2½ | 16⅛ | 1½ | ⅞ | 30- #10 | 29000 | 9900 |

1. Specify the anchor embedment and configuration. See SSTB Anchor Bolts.
2. Allowable loads have been increased 33% for wind or earthquake loading with no further increase allowed; reduce where other load durations govern.

H

CL

W

**I.6**

**S/HD8**

**S/HD10**

**Typical S/HD8 Installation (washer required)**

**Washers are not required for S/HD10.**

---

# S/LTT, S/MTT, S/HTT TENSION TIES

The S/MTT14 and S/HTT14 are single-piece formed tension ties—no rivets, and a 4-ply formed seat which won't unfold during loading. No washers are required.

The S/LTT and S/MTT Tension Ties are ideal for retrofit or new construction projects. They provide high strength, post-pour, concrete-to-steel connections.

**MATERIAL:** See table

**FINISH:** Galvanized.

**INSTALLATION:** ▪ Use all specified fasteners. See Screws, page 4.
▪ Use the specified number and type of screws to attach the strap portion to the steel stud. Bolt the base to the wall or foundation with a suitable anchor; see table for the required bolt diameter.
▪ The S/MTT14 and S/HTT14 can have a maximum offset of 2" from the stud face to the centerline of the anchor bolt.

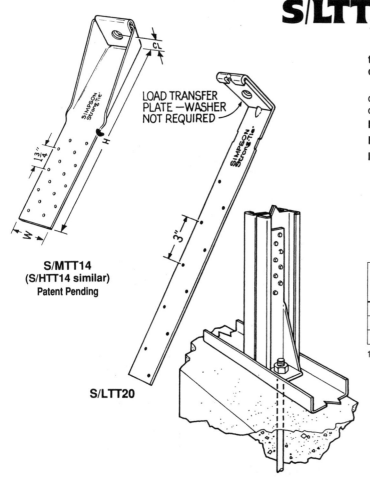

CL

H

1¾"

3"

W

LOAD TRANSFER PLATE—WASHER NOT REQUIRED

SIMPSON Strong-Tie

**S/MTT14 (S/HTT14 similar) Patent Pending**

**S/LTT20**

**Typical S/HTT14 Installation as a Holdown**

| MODEL NO. | MATERIAL | | DIMENSIONS | | | FASTENERS | | ALLOWABLE LOADS (133) |
|---|---|---|---|---|---|---|---|---|
| | STRAP | PLATE | W | H | CL | ANCHOR BOLTS | SCREWS | |
| S/LTT20 | 12 ga | 3 ga | 2 | 20 | 1½ | ½ | 6- #10 | 1750 |
| S/MTT14 | 12 ga | — | 2½ | 15 | 1¹⁄₁₆ | ⅝ | 14- #10 | 4620 |
| S/HTT14 | 11 ga | — | 2½ | 15 | 1¹⁄₁₆ | ⅝ | 16- #10 | 5260 |

1. The designer may specify anchor bolt type, length and embedment.
2. Allowable loads have been increased 33% for wind or earthquake loading with no further increase allowed.

Details and drawings provided courtesy of Simpson Strong-Tie Company, Inc.

# W, WNP HANGERS

This series has the greatest design flexibility and versatility. The hanger's straight side-flanges support the top and bottom of the channel for a strong, balanced connection.

**MATERIAL:** Stirrup—12 gauge

**FINISH:** Simpson gray paint. Some models available hot-dipped galvanized; specify HDG.

**INSTALLATION:** Hangers may be welded to steel headers with ⅛" for W and ³⁄₁₆" for WNP by 1½" fillet welds located at each end of the top flange.

**OPTIONS:** ▪ W and H dimensions are modifiable.

**SLOPED AND/OR SKEWED SEAT**

▪ W/WNP series may be skewed to a maximum of 84° and/or sloped to a maximum of 45°.

▪ For slope only, skew only, or slope and skew combinations, the allowable load is 100% of the table load.

▪ Specify the slope up or down in degrees from the horizontal plane and/or the skew right or left in degrees from the perpendicular vertical plane. Specify whether low side, high side or center of joist will be flush with the top of the header.

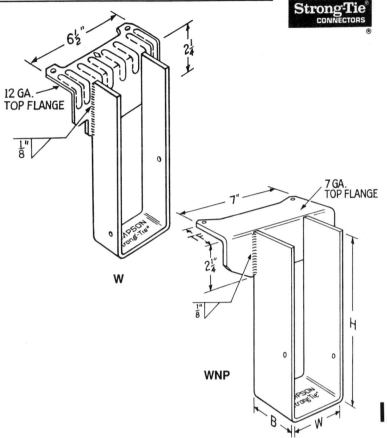

| MODEL NO. | DIMENSIONS | | | FASTENERS | | ALLOWABLE LOADS |
|---|---|---|---|---|---|---|
| | W | H | B | HEADER | JOIST | |
| W | 1⁹⁄₁₆ - 7½ | 3½ - 30 | 2 - 6 | Weld | 2- #10 | 2200 |
| WNP | 1⁹⁄₁₆ - 7½ | 3½ - 30 | 2 - 6 | Weld | 2- #10 | 3255 |

**I.8**

# LB, B HANGERS

Precision forming with manufacturing quality control provides dimensional accuracy and helps ensure proper bearing area and connection. These designs have the material section where it counts, resulting in maximum loads.

**MATERIAL:** LB—14 gauge; B—12 gauge

**FINISH:** Galvanized

**INSTALLATION:** ▪ **LB** may be used for weld-on applications; a minimum of 2" x material thickness of weld on each top flange is required. Distribute the weld equally on both top flanges. Consult the code for special considerations when welding galvanized steel. Uplift loads do not apply to weld-on applications.

▪ **B** may be used for weld-on applications. The minimum required weld to the top flanges is ⅛" x 2" fillet weld to each side of each top flange tab. Distribute the weld equally on both top flanges. Uplift loads do not apply to weld-on applications.

**OPTIONS:** B series can be sloped to a maximum of 45°. For 0° top 30°, the allowable load is 100% of the table load. For 31° to 45°, the maximum allowable download is 80% of the table roof load.

**CODE NUMBER:** ICBO No. 1258.

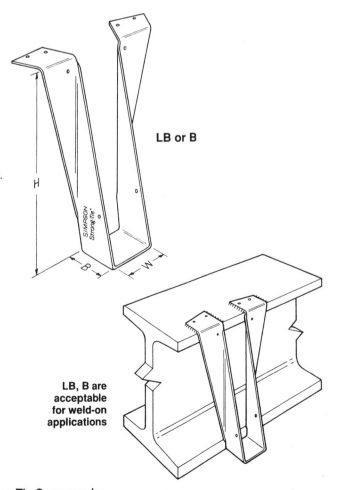

**LB or B**

**LB, B are acceptable for weld-on applications**

| MODEL NO. | DIMENSIONS | | | FASTENERS | | ALLOWABLE LOADS |
|---|---|---|---|---|---|---|
| | W | H | B | HEADER | JOIST | |
| LB | 1⁹⁄₁₆ - 3⁹⁄₁₆ | 3½ - 20 | 2 - 3 | Weld | 2- #10 | 1550 |
| B | 1⁹⁄₁₆ - 7½ | 7 - 30 | 2 - 3 | Weld | 2- #10 | 2415 |

**I.9**

**SIMPSON**
**Strong-Tie®**
**CONNECTORS**

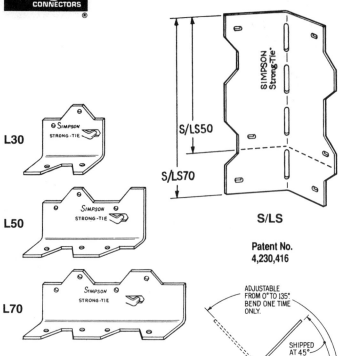

L30

L50

L70

**S/LS**

S/LS50

S/LS70

**Patent No.
4,230,416**

ADJUSTABLE
FROM 0° TO 135°.
BEND ONE TIME
ONLY.

SHIPPED
AT 45°

**S/LS Top View**

# L, S/LS *REINFORCING AND SKEWABLE ANGLES*

General utility reinforcing angles with multiple uses.
S/LS— Field-adjustable angles attach members
intersecting at angles.

**MATERIAL:** L—16 gauge; S/LS—18 gauge

**FINISH:** Galvanized

**INSTALLATION:** ▪ Use all specified fasteners.
See Screws, page 4.

- ▪ S/LS—field-skewable; bend one time only.
- ▪ Joist must be constrained against rotation when
  using a single S/LS per connection.

| MODEL NO. | LENGTH | FASTENERS | ALLOWABLE LOADS | |
|---|---|---|---|---|
| | | | $F_1$ | $F_2$ |
| L30 | 3 | 4- #10 | 255 | 60 |
| L50 | 5 | 6- #10 | 965 | 110 |
| L70 | 7 | 8- #10 | 1375 | 100 |
| S/LS50 | $4^7/_8$ | 4- #10 | 600 | — |
| S/LS70 | $6^3/_8$ | 6- #10 | 915 | — |

1. No load duration increase allowed.
2. Loads are for one part only.
3. L30 loads are based on 20 gauge and heavier members.
   All other loads are based on 16 gauge and heavier members.

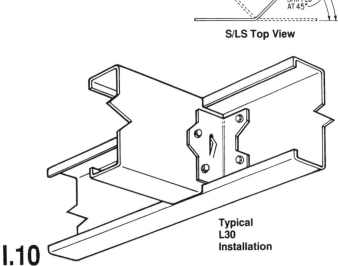

**Typical
L30
Installation**

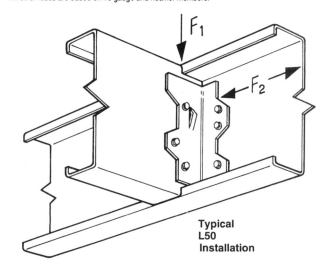

$F_1$

$F_2$

**Typical
L50
Installation**

**I.10**

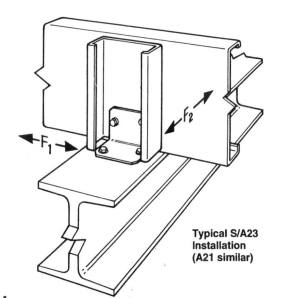

$F_1$

$F_2$

**Typical S/A23
Installation
(A21 similar)**

# A, S/A *ANGLES*

**MATERIAL:** 18 gauge

**FINISH:** Galvanized

**INSTALLATION:** Use all specified fasteners.
See Screws, page 4.

| MODEL NO. | DIMENSIONS | | | FASTENERS | ALLOWABLE[1] LOADS | |
|---|---|---|---|---|---|---|
| | $W_1$ | $W_2$ | L | | $F_1$ | $F_2$ |
| A21 | 2 | $1^1/_2$ | $1^3/_8$ | 4- #10 | 150 | 50 |
| S/A23 | 2 | $1^1/_2$ | $2^3/_4$ | 4- #10 | 310 | 70 |

1. No load duration increase allowed.

**I.11**

# I. HARDWARE / CONNECTORS

## S/H SEISMIC AND HURRICANE TIES

Designed to provide wind and seismic ties for trusses and rafters, this versatile line may be used for general tie purposes, strongback attachments, and as all-purpose ties where one member crosses another.

**MATERIAL:** 18 gauge

**FINISH:** Galvanized. Selected products available in stainless steel or Z-MAX coating; see Corrosion-Resistant Connectors.

**INSTALLATION:** ▪ Use all specified fasteners. See Screws, page 4.
- ▪ The S/H1 can be installed with flanges facing outwards (reverse of illustration #1). When installed inside a wall for truss applications.
- ▪ Ties are shipped in equal quantities of separate rights and lefts.
- ▪ S/H1 does not replace solid blocking.

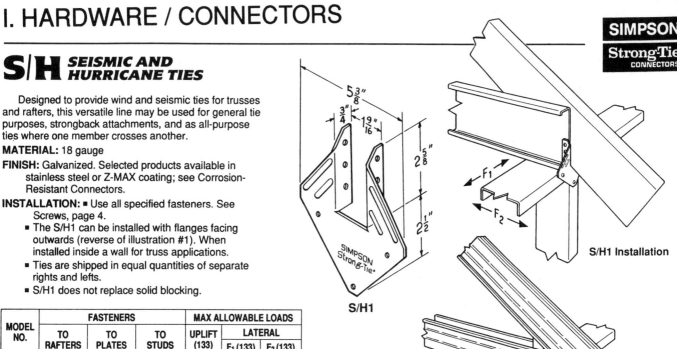

S/H1

S/H1 Installation

S/H1 Installation

| MODEL NO. | FASTENERS | | | MAX ALLOWABLE LOADS | | |
|---|---|---|---|---|---|---|
| | TO RAFTERS | TO PLATES | TO STUDS | UPLIFT (133) | LATERAL | |
| | | | | | F₁ (133) | F₂ (133) |
| S/H1 | 3- #10 | 2- #10 | 1- #10 | 330 | 100 | 115 |
| S/H2 | 3- #10 | — | 3- #10 | 395 | — | — |
| S/H2.5 | 4- #10 | — | 4- #10 | 415 | 90 | 125 |
| S/H3 | 2- #10 | 2- #10 | — | 380 | 90 | 125 |

1. Loads have been increased 33% for wind or earthquake loading; no further increase allowed.

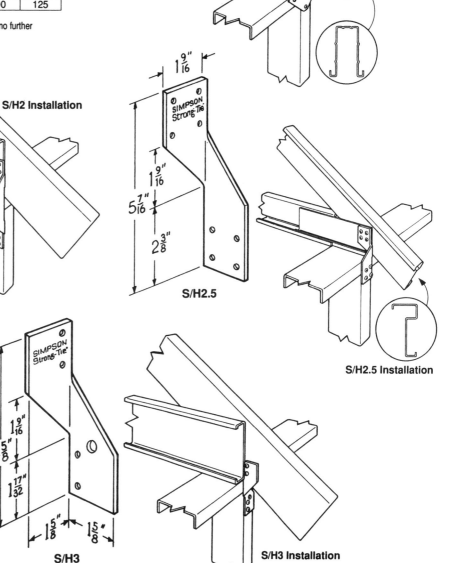

S/H2 Installation

S/H2

S/H2.5

S/H2.5 Installation

S/H3

S/H3 Installation

**I.12**

# LTS, MTS *TWIST STRAPS*

Twist straps provide a tension connection between two members. These 1¼″ wide straps are an economical way to resist uplift at the heel of a truss.

The 3″ bend section eliminates interference at the transition points.

**MATERIAL:** MTS—16 gauge; LTS—18 gauge

**FINISH:** Galvanized. Selected products available in stainless steel and Z-MAX coating; see Corrosion-Resistant Connectors.

**INSTALLATION:** Use all specified fasteners. See Screws, page 4.

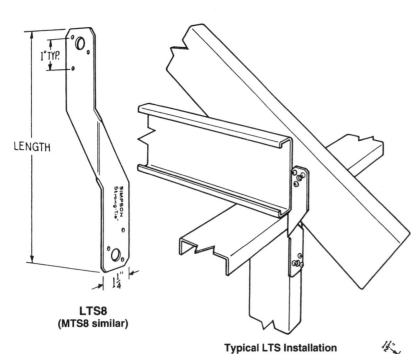

| MODEL NO. | LENGTH | FASTENERS (TOTAL) | ALLOWABLE LOADS (133) |
|---|---|---|---|
| LTS8 | 8 | 6- #10 | 400 |
| MTS8 | 8 | 6- #10 | 640 |

1. Install half of the fasteners on each end of the strap to achieve full loads.
2. Loads have been increased 33% for wind or earthquake loading with no further increase allowed.

**LTS8**
**(MTS8 similar)**

**Typical LTS Installation
Truss to Steel Studs**

## I.13

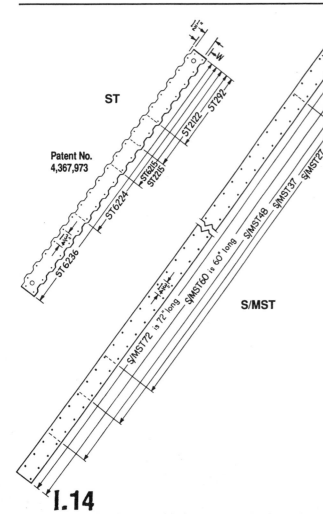

**ST**

**Patent No.
4,367,973**

**S/MST**

# ST, S/MST *STRAP TIES*

Install Strap Ties where plates or soles are cut, at wall intersections, floor-to-floor applications, and as ridge ties and truss plates.

**FINISH:** Galvanized.

**INSTALLATION:** Use all specified fasteners. See Screws, page 4.

| MODEL NO. | MATL | DIMENSIONS | | FASTENERS (TOTAL) | ALLOWABLE LOADS (133) |
|---|---|---|---|---|---|
| | | W | L | | |
| ST292 | 20 ga | 2¹⁄₁₆ | 9⁵⁄₁₆ | 8- #10 | 1075 |
| ST2122 | 20 ga | 2¹⁄₁₆ | 12¹³⁄₁₆ | 10- #10 | 1425 |
| ST2115 | 20 ga | ¾ | 16⁵⁄₁₆ | 4- #10 | 600 |
| ST2215 | 20 ga | 2¹⁄₁₆ | 16⁵⁄₁₆ | 10- #10 | 1615 |
| ST6215 | 16 ga | 2¹⁄₁₆ | 16⁵⁄₁₆ | 12- #10 | 1785 |
| ST6224 | 16 ga | 2¹⁄₁₆ | 23⁵⁄₁₆ | 16- #10 | 2500 |
| ST6236 | 14 ga | 2¹⁄₁₆ | 33¹³⁄₁₆ | 22- #10 | 3300 |
| S/MST27 | 12 ga | 2¹⁄₁₆ | 27 | 18- #10 | 2675 |
| S/MST37 | 12 ga | 2¹⁄₁₆ | 37 | 24- #10 | 3745 |
| S/MST48 | 12 ga | 2¹⁄₁₆ | 48 | 28- #10 | 4460 |
| S/MST60 | 10 ga | 2¹⁄₁₆ | 60 | 36- #10 | 5800 |
| S/MST72 | 10 ga | 2¹⁄₁₆ | 72 | 36- #10 | 5800 |

1. Maximum loads have been increased for wind or earthquake loading with no further increase allowed.

## I.14

**Details and drawings provided courtesy of Simpson Strong-Tie Company, Inc.**

# I. HARDWARE / CONNECTORS

# CS, CMST *COILED STRAPS*

CS are continuous utility straps which can be cut to length on the job site. Packaged in a lightweight (about 40 pounds), portable 2' square carton. The popular 18 gauge strap is available in 100' or 200' rolls—specify CS18-100 or CS18-200.

**MATERIAL**: See table

**FINISH**: Galvanized. Selected products available in Z-MAX; see Corrosion-Resistant Connectors.

**INSTALLATION**: ■ Use all specified fasteners. See Screws pg 4.
■ The table shows the maximum allowable loads and the screws required to obtain them. Fewer screws may be used; reduce the allowable load by the code lateral load for each screw subtracted from each end.

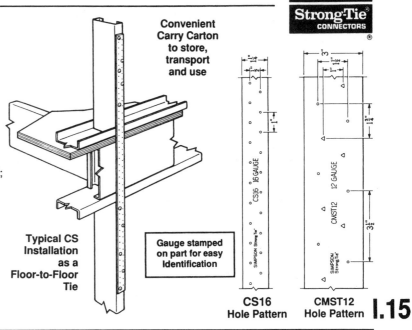

**Convenient Carry Carton to store, transport and use**

**Typical CS Installation as a Floor-to-Floor Tie**

**Gauge stamped on part for easy Identification**

| MODEL NO. | MATERIAL | TOTAL LENGTH | TOTAL FASTENERS | ALLOWABLE LOADS (133) |
|---|---|---|---|---|
| CMST12 | 12 ga | 40' | 60- #10 | 9640 |
| CS16 | 16 ga | 150' | 12- #10 | 1650 |
| CS18 | 18 ga | 100' & 200' | 8- #10 | 1270 |
| CS20 | 20 ga | 250' | 8- #10 | 1005 |
| CS22 | 22 ga | 300' | 6- #10 | 825 |

1. 133% value may be used for wind or earthquake loading.

**CS16 Hole Pattern**  **CMST12 Hole Pattern** **I.15**

# PSC *PLYWOOD SHEATHING CLIPS*

**MATERIAL:** 18 gauge
**FINISH:** Galvanized
**INSTALLATION:** Models (sizes) available are ⅜ PSC, ⁷⁄₁₆ PSC, ¹⁵⁄₃₂ PSC, ½ PSC, ¹⁹⁄₃₂ PSC, ⅝ PSC, and ¾ PSC.

| SPAN RATING | PLYWOOD THICKNESS | MAXIMUM SPAN | | PSCs PER SPAN |
|---|---|---|---|---|
| | | WITH PSCs | WITHOUT PSCs | |
| 24/0 | ⅜, ⁷⁄₁₆ | 24 | 20 | 1 |
| 32/16 | ¹⁵⁄₃₂, ½, ⅝ | 32 | 28 | 1 |
| 40/20 | ¹⁹⁄₃₂, ⅝, ¾ | 40 | 32 | 1 |
| 48/24 | ¾ | 48 | 36 | 2 |

1. Span ratings for APA Rated Sheathing when the long dimension or strength axis is across three or more supports.

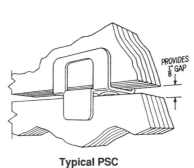

**PROVIDES ⅛" GAP**

**Typical PSC Installation**

**EMBOSSED FOR AUTOMATIC SPACING**  SIMPSON Strong-Tie  **PSC** **I.16**

# TB, LTB *BRIDGING*

TB—Tension-type bridging with maximum fastener flexibility. Use two of the seven screw holes at each end.

LTB—Staggered fastener pattern accommodates 6" to 12" web height. Use two of the holes at each end.

**MATERIAL:** LTB—22 gauge; TB—20 gauge
**FINISH:** Galvanized
**INSTALLATION:** Bridging will fit flange widths from 1⅝ to 3".

| WEB HEIGHT | SPACING | TB | | LTB |
|---|---|---|---|---|
| | | MODEL NO. | L | MODEL NO. |
| 6" | 12" o.c. | TB20 | 20 | LTB20 |
| 8" | 12" o.c. | TB20 | 20 | LTB20 |
| 10" | 12" o.c. | TB20 | 20 | LTB20 |
| 12" | 12" o.c. | TB27 | 27 | — |
| 6" | 16" o.c. | TB27 | 27 | — |
| 8" | 16" o.c. | TB27 | 27 | — |
| 10" | 16" o.c. | TB27 | 27 | — |
| 12" | 16" o.c. | TB27 | 27 | — |
| 6" | 24" o.c. | TB36 | 36 | — |
| 8" | 24" o.c. | TB36 | 36 | — |
| 10" | 24" o.c. | TB36 | 36 | — |
| 12" | 24" o.c. | TB36 | 36 | — |

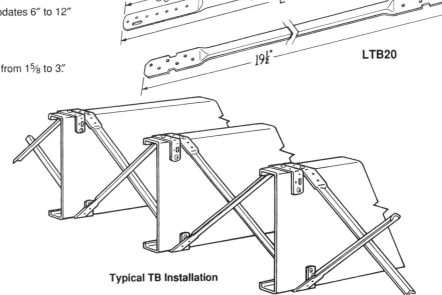

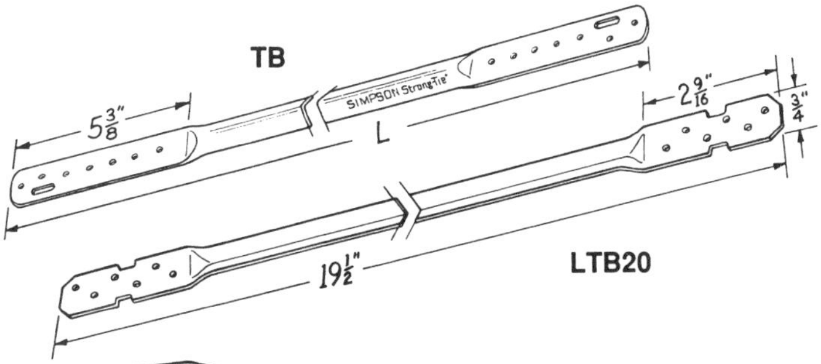

**TB**  **LTB20**

**Typical TB Installation**

Details and drawings provided courtesy of Simpson Strong-Tie Company, Inc. **I.17**

# I. HARDWARE / CONNECTORS

## U.S. Standard Steel Gauge Equivalents in Nominal Dimensions

| GAUGE | APPROXIMATE DIMENSIONS | | DECIMALS (INCHES) | | |
|-------|------|------|------------------|-------------------|-------|
|       | in | mm | UNCOATED STEEL | GALVANIZED STEEL (G60) | Z-MAX™ |
| 3  | ¼    | 6   | 0.239″ | —      | —      |
| 7  | ³⁄₁₆ | 4.5 | 0.179″ | —      | —      |
| 10 | ⁹⁄₆₄ | 3.4 | 0.134″ | 0.138″ | 0.140″ |
| 11 | ⅛    | 3   | 0.120″ | 0.123″ | 0.125″ |
| 12 | ⁷⁄₆₄ | 2.7 | 0.105″ | 0.108″ | 0.110″ |
| 14 | ⁵⁄₆₄ | 2   | 0.075″ | 0.078″ | 0.080″ |
| 16 | ¹⁄₁₆ | 1.5 | 0.060″ | 0.063″ | 0.065″ |
| 18 | ³⁄₆₄ | 1.2 | 0.048″ | 0.052″ | 0.054″ |
| 20 | ¹⁄₃₂ | 1   | 0.036″ | 0.040″ | 0.042″ |
| 22 | ¹⁄₃₂ | 0.8 | 0.030″ | 0.034″ | 0.036″ |

1. Actual steel dimensions will vary from nominal dimensions according to industry tolerances.

## Bolt Diameter Conversion

| in | mm |
|----|------|
| ⅜  | 9.5  |
| ½  | 12.7 |
| ⅝  | 15.9 |
| ¾  | 19.1 |
| ⅞  | 22.2 |
| 1  | 25.4 |

## Metric Conversion Chart

| IMPERIAL | METRIC |
|----------|----------|
| 1 in  | 25.40 mm |
| 1 ft  | 0.3048 m |
| 1 lb  | 4.448 N  |
| 1 Kip | 4.448 kN |
| 1 psi | 6895 Pa  |

mm = millimeter
m = meter
N = newton
kN = kilonewton
Pa = pascal

## Roof Slope Conversion Chart

| RISE/RUN | SLOPE |
|----------|-------|
| 1/12  | 5°  |
| 2/12  | 10° |
| 3/12  | 14° |
| 4/12  | 18° |
| 5/12  | 23° |
| 6/12  | 27° |
| 7/12  | 30° |
| 8/12  | 34° |
| 9/12  | 37° |
| 10/12 | 40° |
| 11/12 | 42° |
| 12/12 | 45° |

Slope rounded to the nearest degree.

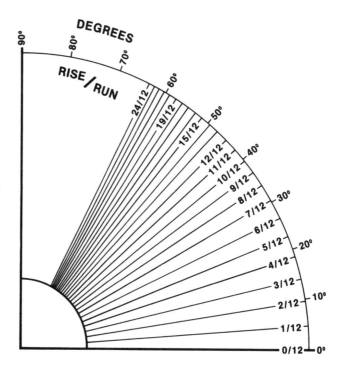

# NOW AVAILABLE !

## STEEL FRAMING BLUEPRINTS

Complete sample reference blueprints for single story and two story steel framed designed homes. An Excellent source for architects, engineers and contractors looking for an easy reference to the construction of steel framing in single family constuction. These plans utilize the details contained in the **Residential Steel Framing Construction Guide** and provide the guidelines and format necessary for building department approvals.

Each plan comes with wall panel layout, second floor framing plan (two story), roof framing plan and corresponding detail sheets. Plans are available in half size sheets only for quick reference and easy storage in your briefcase or desk.

Single story - $19.95 plus $4.00 shipping and handling (add $1.00 for each additional plan shipped).
Two story - $24.95 plus $4.00 shipping and handling (add $1.00 for each additional plan shipped).

NOTE: Each plan has been through plan check and received Building Dept. approval.
**A 10% discount is available when ordering both plans.**

-------------------------------------------------------------------------------------------------------

## ORDER FORM

Name:_____ Address:_____

State:_____ Zip Code:_____ Tel#:_____ Credit card#_____

Mcard __ Visa__ Exp. date_____ Quantity Ordered: ___ Single story ___ Two story

Send check or money order to Technical Publications 1442 E. Lincoln Ave., Orange CA 92665. California residents add 7.75% sales tax. Prices and availability are subject to change without notice. **Visa and Mastercard accepted.** Allow up to 4 weeks delivery.

# NOW AVAILABLE !

## STEEL FRAMING BLUEPRINTS

Complete sample reference blueprints for single story and two story steel framed designed homes. An Excellent source for architects, engineers and contractors looking for an easy reference to the construction of steel framing in single family constuction. These plans utilize the details contained in the **Residential Steel Framing Construction Guide** and provide the guidelines and format necessary for building department approvals.

Each plan comes with wall panel layout, second floor framing plan (two story), roof framing plan and corresponding detail sheets. Plans are available in half size sheets only for quick reference and easy storage in your briefcase or desk.

Single story - $19.95 plus $4.00 shipping and handling (add $1.00 for each additional plan shipped).

Two story - $24.95 plus $4.00 shipping and handling (add $1.00 for each additional plan shipped).

NOTE: Each plan has been through plan check and received Building Dept. approval. **A 10% discount is available when ordering both plans.**

-------------------------------------------------------------------------------------------

## ORDER FORM

Name:_____ Address:_____

State:____ Zip Code:_____ Tel#:_____ Credit card#_____

Mcard __ Visa__ Exp. date_____ Quantity Ordered: ___ Single story ___ Two story

Send check or money order to Technical Publications 1442 E. Lincoln Ave., Orange CA 92665. California residents add 7.75% sales tax. Prices and availability are subject to change without notice. **Visa and Mastercard accepted.** Allow up to 4 weeks delivery.

| | | |
|---|---|---|
| 2 1/2 x 10 | STUD | 1.79 |
| 2 1/2 x 9 | STUD | 1.59 |
| 3 5/8 x 10 | " | 2.05 |
| 3 5/8 x 9 | " | 1.89 |
| 3 5/8 x 8 | " | 1.69 |
| 2 1/2 x 8 | " | 1.45 |
| 2 1/2 x 10 | TRACK | 1.84 |
| 3 5/8 x 10 | " | 2.09 |